FM

MISS FANNIE MAE'S GIRLS

A NOVEL BY LARRY BATCHELOR

WWW.3LPUBLISHING.COM

The information contained in this book is intended to be educational and not for diagnosis, prescription, or treatment of any health disorder whatsoever. This book is sold with the understanding that neither the author nor publisher is engaged in rendering any legal, psychological, or accounting advice. The publisher and author disclaim personal liability, directly or indirectly, for advice of information presented within. Although the author and publisher have prepared this manuscript with utmost care and diligence and have made every effort to ensure the accuracy and completeness of the information contained within, we assume no responsibility for errors, inaccuracies, omissions or inconsistencies.

Library of Congress Control Number: 2011928899

ISBN-13: 9780615562407

Miss Fannie Mae's Girls soft-cover edition 2011

Printed in the United States of America

For more information about special discounts for bulk purchases, please contact 3L Publishing at 916.300.8012 or log onto our website at www.3LPublishing.com.

Author photo by Martin Regusters-Leaping Lion Photography

Book design by Erin Pace-Molina

Cover photo by Jack Delano, June 1941 from the Library of Congress Photo Collection, Farm Security Administration - Office of War Information Collection
11671-10 (DLC) 93845501

DEDICATION

Dedicated in loving memory of my grandmother

Rosalie Kleckly Batchelor
1907 - 1993

CONTENTS

PROLOGUE

Fannie Mae Jessup Turner, like my grandmother Rosalie Kleckly Batchelor, was born in the city of Oglethorpe on the banks of the Flint River in Macon County, Georgia. Unlike my grandmother, Miss Fannie Mae never made it out of Oglethorpe, Georgia. On the other hand, my grandmother Miss Rosalie left and returned only once. The memories of her birthplace were so painful that she found it difficult to talk about with her children and grandchildren. She ran away from the bigotry, anger, hatred and despair that were experienced by black folks throughout the segregated South.

Rosalie was a striking Negro woman with skin the color of dark mahogany and long, silky medium-brown hair that came from her Native-American heritage. Her husband James was extremely fair skinned with keen features and a mixed ethnic blend of Negro, Scottish and Irish. James and his parents could pass for white in the rural south, but there was no mistaking Rosalie's background and ethnicity. Because of this glaring contrast between the two of them, they were viewed as an interracial couple by some. Racial intolerance and bigotry forced them to move north to Philadelphia in 1922. Rosalie returned to Oglethorpe, Georgia in 1929 to visit the family she had left behind. With her, she had three small children with light skin and curly blonde hair in tow. Once again, she was subjected to more of the racial intolerance and bigotry and was forced to leave her birthplace in Macon County for good. Many folks who did not know her assumed that she had bore these children with a Caucasian man. As a result, she never returned to the South, and she never crossed the Mason-Dixon Line again.

Rosalie eventually brought her mother, father and four of her younger siblings up north to live. Her only immediate family members left in South Georgia were two older sisters who were already too settled with families of their own to relocate. They wrote letters and sent pictures. Rosalie never saw her eldest sister again, and she only saw her next-to-oldest sister once at another sister's funeral in Cincinnati, Ohio.

Oglethorpe, Georgia in Macon County is of significant importance in the story of Fannie Mae Turner. It not only shaped her environment and her surroundings, it also had a strong influence on events that formed her life. It is where she was born, met her husband, buried her mother, and gave birth to and raised her children — and it is where she died. It is also where she lost her father mysteriously to the Ku Klux Klan. It is where the voices of spirits, both black and white, still echo with resentment all the way from the burial grounds to the limbs of tall oak trees.

Like many generations of Negroes who remained in the South, Fannie Mae and her family endured the injustices, indignities and hatred directed at them by whites. The social stigma of being thought of as "inferior beings" dated back to when slaves were first brought over from Africa. These slaves were now living in a strange land, being deprived of the benefits of a basic education, and facing a language barrier that made things even more difficult. These people of color who came from across a wide expanse of ocean were at a disadvantage from the time that they landed on American soil. They were treated harshly and called "Niggers" and "Coons." They were spit upon, degraded and demeaned. Later they were called African-American. The African part of them was mostly obvious except for those who were sired by white slave masters; but the American part of them was always elusive and never quite evident. Many who were "high born" to slave women and white slave masters were known as "House Niggers" and the others were field hands. The offspring of Thomas Jefferson and Sally Hemings were prime examples of mixed race slaves.

After the indignities of slavery, the freed Negro people of the Old South were still considered to be underclass citizens and continued to suffer at the hands of white men who harbored anger and animosity toward them, particularly members of the Ku Klux Klan. They were victims of lynching, mutilation, debasement, and moral and social degradation. They were ostracized second-class citizens in their new homeland that was supposed to be the "Land of the Free." It became a normal way of life for them; they knew no other. Over time the descendants of the once-docile African slaves morphed into non-violent protestors during the Civil Rights Movement, and eventually they became men and women who would stand tall and be free.

It was the same in Oglethorpe, Georgia as it was in Selma, Alabama and throughout the rest of the South. People who were poor, uneducated and suppressed never seemed to find the exit. They never found a way out but they remained forever committed to their faith in God and remained hopeful that one day they too would be free. Their freedom eventually came at a very heavy price.

In the case of Fannie Mae Turner and many like her in Macon County, Georgia, they found freedom in their churches, their community, and in their strong belief in God. That which made their lives more difficult and unbearable also made them stronger. In the face of adversity, hardship, struggles and heartbreak, they managed to survive through their faith and their resilience. Fannie Mae Turner was a survivor in the midst of trials and tribulations. She always managed to maintain a positive attitude and outlook on life — this she learned from her mother. Her mother Jesse taught her to be strong and resilient — and these traits she passed on to her daughters, "Miss Fannie Mae's Girls."

CHAPTER 1

THE BUCK STOPS HERE (BUCK, JESSE, FANNIE MAE AND THE KLAN)

Fannie Mae Turner died on New Year's Eve, December 31, 2008. She was the daughter of sharecroppers. She was born in a shack on a dusty, dirt road in the backwoods of Macon County, Georgia in 1922. Fannie Mae had skin the color of red Georgia clay. On the day she was born her mother screamed, not because of the difficult childbirth, but for the mere fact that her baby girl was the color of dirt with eyes as black as coal dust. A local Oglethorpe midwife delivered her. Afterward the newborn child was a frightening sight — all covered in the afterbirth, blood and placenta.

Fannie Mae died from fright that night. Her weakened heart gave out when she heard gunshots that were too near to where she slept on that New Year's Eve. Each year, she dreaded the holidays when revelers felt the need to make loud noises. She hated the firecrackers and fireworks on the Fourth of July. And, she especially feared the sounds of gunfire on New Year's Eve.

Fannie Mae used to say to her family, "Just listen to those no-count fools making all of that ruckus. Ain't they got nothing better to do than to wake the dead?"

As she grew older, she became more frightened and annoyed by the antics of "hooligans" as she used to call them. Fannie Mae found it hard to fall asleep as the midnight hour approached on New Year's Eve. She was always afraid that a stray bullet might somehow find its way into her home. Before she became ill, she would be in church until all of the noise settled down; but on the night that she died, she was alone in her house when she heard gunfire from revelers in cars passing by on the road and gunshots far off in the distance. She became startled and died instantly.

She died beneath her favorite quilt, the one that she and her mama Jesse had made with their own hands. Some folks say that Fannie Mae was always afraid of the sound of guns going off since that was the last sound she remembered as a little girl when her daddy was taken away by the Ku Klux Klan, never to return to their sharecropper's farm. She never knew what had actually happened to her father until her mother told her when she was old enough to understand. And even then she found it hard to comprehend.

"How could people be so cruel and evil?" she had asked her mother Jesse.

Her mother shook her head in silence. She had no answers for her daughter, only prayers that things would one day in the future change for the better.

It was in the month of July in the summer of 1927. She was just five years old when she heard the sound of cars rolling on the hard mud-caked road leading up to their old farmhouse. Fannie Mae heard her daddy Buck say to her mother Jesse, "Get the baby and go on out yonder to the shed. Stay there 'til I comes and gets you."

It was about midnight, and the moon was nearly full. Her mother came to her in the dark, scooped her up in her arms, and carried her out the back door of the house. The woodshed was located on the backside of the smokehouse about 100 yards away. Jesse was barefoot as she ran with her daughter to safety under the lean-to. She covered Fannie Mae's mouth to keep the child from crying out loud. There they stayed quietly crouched, waiting for Buck to give a sign that it was clear for them to come back. The night air was hot, sticky and muggy. Mosquitoes swarmed all around them, attacked, and bit Jesse and Fannie Mae. Despite the irritations, Jesse remained still even though the many bug bites made her uncomfortable. She wrapped her nightgown around her daughter's body like a mosquito net for protection. And, she kept her hand firmly clamped over the child's mouth.

The signal from Buck never came. Instead, in the still of the night they heard many men talking and shouting in angry voices, including the voice of Buck Jessup.

"Buck Jessup! Get your nigger ass out here right now!" said one voice.

"If-in you don't, we is fixing to come and get you," hollered another.

"We is going to burn you and your family out," shouted a third voice.

"Let's go in and get him," shouted another.

"You best get on out here boy!"

The door slowly creaked open. Buck Jessup stood in the doorway with his shotgun in hand. He stared down about eight or nine hooded and robed men. The bright moonlight cast silhouettes and shadows of the angry mob standing before him.

"Go on way from here! I don't wants no trouble," said Buck.

He had recognized some of the voices, but dared not call out their names. Buck Jessup feared for his life and safety of his wife and young daughter. One of the voices that he recognized was that of Sheriff Mack Murray. Another was the voice of Tom Meade, owner of the Oglethorpe General Store. A third and unmistakable voice was that of Robert Brown whose family owned the land adjacent to the Jessup farm. There had been a long-running dispute over the boundary lines between their properties. Robert Brown had threatened Buck Jessup many times. And, many times Buck reported the threats to Sheriff Mack Murray, to no avail.

Four of the men walked up on the porch where Buck stood with their guns pointed at him. He did not stand a chance, so he placed his shotgun down on the porch floor. He was a peaceful and God-fearing man. He would go peacefully to protect his family. He somehow knew that he would never see them again. The four men grabbed Buck and threw him to the ground. During the ensuing struggle, the hood covering the head of one the men came off. It fell to the dirt just as Buck looked up. He was staring right in the face of Sheriff Mack Murray.

There were two gunshots. Jesse tried to cover Fannie Mae's ears. It was too late — her little girl had heard sounds that no child should ever have to hear. There was silence until Jesse heard the sound of the cars leaving back down the dirt road from the Jessup farm. Fearing the worst, Jesse Jessup stayed hidden with Fannie Mae until daybreak. She walked slowly around the smokehouse, carrying her sleeping child. She had no time to consider the many mosquito bites the two of them had endured during their night outdoors. There were only the thoughts of what had occurred the night before. When she arrived at the front of the house, Buck's shotgun lay on the front porch — and the door to the house was wide open, her husband Buck gone.

Like so many other Negro men, the case of the missing and presumed-dead Buck Jessup was never solved in Macon County, Georgia. Local folks had their ideas of what had happened to him, but they only spoke about it quietly and in private. The Klan had buried many bodies so that they would never be found. Rumor was that the bauxite mines around Macon County held the key to the mysterious disappearances and the whereabouts of so-called "Uppity Niggers." In order to justify the disappearance of black men without a trace, the invisible members of the Ku Klux Klan (aka the KKK) made sure that they were falsely accused of rape, robbery or burglary. It was then surmised that the men simply fled in order to avoid prosecution. They paid white women to accuse black men of rape. Local merchants identified them as robbery suspects, and white homeowners accused them of burglary. It was a no-win situation with the Macon County Sheriff at the center of the investigation.

Whenever Jesse went to the Oglethorpe General Store, Tom Meade always said to her, "Lord Miss Jessup, I sure hopes Sheriff Murray helps you find out what is done happen to Buck. He was a fine man, a good ole boy!"

Whenever she saw Sheriff Murray, he tipped his hat and said, "Howdy Miss Jessup, we is still a looking for Buck. God bless you now!"

Jesse Jessup just nodded her head and kept walking in silence. She had her suspicions that Mack Murray knew more than he let on. Buck used to always tell her, "If anything was to happen to me, you keep one eye on that sheriff."

Mack Murray was married to Robert Brown's sister Sally Belle. The two brothers-in-law were very close.

Jesse Jessup mysteriously never heard another word from Robert Brown about the property line or the boundaries of her land.

Fannie Mae's mother Jesse continued to work the fields and bring in the crops at harvest time. When Fannie Mae was old enough, she joined her mother in the fields. She rose before dawn to get her chores done before heading off to the one-room schoolhouse where she walked each morning. She was the only girl who had hands as rough and calloused as the boys she attended school with. They too worked and plowed the fields with their folks. It wasn't considered ladylike for a girl to work so hard, but her mother was too stubborn and proud to ask the nearby men folk for help. After the KKK had taken her daddy

Buck, her mother would not allow any men colored or white to ever come near their house again, unless they were relatives. She was known to have run off the Watkins and Fuller Brush salesmen with Buck's shotgun.

Fannie Mae always daydreamed that one day she would "get the hell away from Macon County." She wanted to move upstate to Atlanta. She never made it out. Instead, she married her second cousin Henry Turner and bore him eight children. Three of their children died at childbirth. The three who died were all boys. Fannie Mae always believed that there was a curse put on her family by the Klan. No male child would ever be born to live on the same land that her father had died on. No male child would ever live to work the land that Buck Jessup disappeared from. And, no man would ever be taken away from her again; however, God saw fit to take her beloved Henry away in the summer of 1992.

Henry Turner was a loving and caring husband and father. He protected his wife and daughters from the evils of the world around them. He provided for their welfare and well being — and he never complained. While he was strict as far as his daughters were concerned, he always knew that they were raised in the right way. By most accounts everyone who knew him thought that Henry Turner was firm yet fair — and he was a good provider for his family. He was a rock and pillar not only for his family, but also in the Oglethorpe community and his church. Henry and Fannie Mae were devoted members of New Ebenezer First Missionary Baptist Church. They and their children were all baptized in the church.

Fannie Mae and Henry Turner had five daughters. Their names were Belle, Nettie, Rosalie, Christine and Elenora. They raised their daughters very much in the same way that Fannie's mother had raised her — to be God-fearing, hard-working girls who knew how to be strong when called upon. Each girl was as different as her name. Belle, the oldest, was called "Lil Buck" after her grandpa Buck. Nettie, the second girl, was nicknamed "Sis." Rosalie was called "Big Red," because she was the same color as her mother. Christine was called "Sweetie Pie." And, Elenora went by the name "Girlie."

The two eldest, Belle and Nettie, remained in Macon County, Georgia. Rosalie moved to Albany, Georgia. Christine relocated to Atlanta to fulfill the dream that her mother Fannie Mae always had. Elenora moved to New York and changed her name to Lena to pursue her own dream of becoming a stage actress, singer and dancer. She eventually made it to Broadway dancing in a chorus line. She became a lounge singer of note, singing in jazz clubs and speakeasies. Lena never got her big break — her big dream was to star in a Broadway musical, singing, dancing and acting. But, nonetheless, "Girlie" became the star of the family. Or, so she said!

CHAPTER 2

SUNDAY SUPPERS AT FANNIE MAE TURNER'S (NO POSSUM IN HER POT)

Belle, who lived just through a clearing in the woods from Fannie Mae's house, found her mother's cold, stiff body under the quilt that ordinarily kept her snug and warm at night. It was New Year's Day, January 1, 2009. Belle walked through the path to her mother's house to prepare her morning meal and sit and talk about the days gone by. This had become a daily ritual ever since Fannie Mae had taken ill almost a year earlier. They spent hours catching up on the news from the outside world and the latest gossip from around Oglethorpe and Macon County, Georgia. There was always something new for Belle to tell Fannie Mae — and Fannie Mae looked forward to her daily briefings. Belle enjoyed every minute of her visits with her mother. Belle returned in the early evening each day to bring dinner to her mother and stay until her bedtime.

Up until the time that Fannie Mae took ill, she was full of life and energy. She went to church on Sundays and prepared a truly Southern meal after worship service for Belle, who had never married, and her other daughter Nettie and husband, Joe Bamo. The Sunday supper almost always consisted of homemade biscuits, rolls or cornbread, baked hen and dressing, string beans, yellow squash and pole beans. On occasion, Fannie Mae baked a pound cake or made rice or bread pudding.

During the summer months, she found energy and time to make fresh-churned peach or strawberry ice cream. And, during the winter, she cooked chitlins and hog maws at least once. This was a true testament to how much Fannie Mae loved her family. Just cleaning and cooking chitlins and maws is a monumental task. She cleaned the chitlins on Saturday, and then slow cooked them on Sunday while she was at church. Once her cousin Mattie Jo, who had never cleaned chitlins before, put them in her wringer-washer and completely destroyed the meal and ruined the machine. Mattie Jo decided to stick to cooking the possums, squirrels and raccoons that her husband, Tump Kleckly, shot and brought home.

Chitlins, originally known as a poor man's staple, over time became a meal served in some fancy restaurants up north accompanied by champagne; but Fannie Mae served chitlins the old-fashioned way with southern sweet iced tea, collard greens and cornbread.

Fannie Mae always had enough food just in case Pastor Hicks and his wife, Ethel, stopped by after church. She loved cooking and received great pleasure when there were extra guests at her table. Her daughter Rosalie, Rosalie's husband, Esau Tate, and their very effeminate son, Marshall, often drove up from Albany, Georgia every third Sunday of the month. Rosalie and Marshall were loud and boisterous, making the family gatherings congenial and lots of fun. Only Christine and Elenora were missing. They seldom visited the home place in South Georgia, but telephoned their mother as often as possible. Fannie Mae always looked forward to their telephone calls. Christine told her about the city of Atlanta and described how it was constantly growing so big.

"Before long, Atlanta will be as big as New York City," she said to Fannie Mae.

Elenora told her mother about all of the new plays that were opening on Broadway and the latest gossip from the "Big Apple."

Fannie Mae sometimes closed her eyes and visualized what those two cities were like. She often wondered how her two youngest daughters ever managed to live outside of South Georgia in such big cities and among such chaos. Maybe it was easier for the younger generation. Her three older daughters never showed any interest in moving too far away.

Christine "Sweetie Pie" was an odd duck who had awkward mannerisms and expressions. She was always mispronouncing and misusing her words. She thought that by getting away from Macon County and going up to Atlanta was somehow like getting out of Georgia altogether. She always talked as if the people who she had left behind back home in Oglethorpe, including Fannie Mae, were just country bumpkins — and that she was the worldly and sophisticated one. Truth be told, Christine was just as country as they come. She arrived in Atlanta with three gold teeth in the front of her mouth and the oily curl activator from her Jheri-curled hair, which dripped all over and stained her powder-blue polyester pantsuit and yellow floral print blouse. She thought that she was bad to the bone with her Mary Jane pumps that were all run over at the heels from walking the dirt roads of Macon County and strutting her stuff around the town square in Oglethorpe, Georgia on a Friday night.

On the other hand, Elenora "Girlie" — now known as Lena Turner — was by far the most sophisticated of Fannie Mae's daughters. She had a style all her own that did not come naturally, but from reading movie magazines, the *National Enquirer, Ebony, Jet* and *Essence.* Whenever Elenora called Fannie Mae, she reminded her mother never to call her "Girlie" again.

"Mama my name is Lena, Lena Turner!" Elenora "Girlie" Turner died the day she boarded a Greyhound bus for New York City to find her fortune and fame. Whenever she pronounced her newly adopted name, she immediately thought of herself as a cross between Lana Turner and Lena Horne. She somehow fancied herself as a little bit of both. She conjured up visions of playing Lana's role in "Imitation of Life" or Lena's role in "Cabin in the Sky."

As a young woman, Elenora spent every spare dime that she had on movie magazines, Nadinola, Ambi and Artra skin-tone creams. She would hold up a picture of Lana Turner or Lena Horne next to her face in the mirror to compare her skin-lightening success. If she couldn't be as white as Lana Turner, she at least wanted to be as light, bright and damn near white like Lena Horne. And, did she ever spend many hours in front of that mirror. Every one of her sisters simply humored her just for the fun of it.

"Girlie, you sure enough white child!" they would say with their fingers crossed behind their backs, so as not to be caught by God for telling a fib.

And now that Fannie Mae had died, her five girls faced the reality of making plans for her funeral. They would also all be under the same roof once again. The five very different and eccentric personalities would want five different ways to honor their dearly departed mother, Fannie Mae. Unbeknownst to them, Fannie Mae had planned her own funeral. She feared that left up to her family, she would have a funeral cortege with a horse-drawn carriage, and her daughter Elenora running behind it crying, "Mama please don't leave me," just like in "Imitation of Life." Or even worse, they would let her grandson, Marshall, make the plans for her funeral, as if he was making a float for a Gay Pride parade. She used to imagine that Marshall put her body in the brightest pink casket and made her wear a lavender gown with a fuchsia feather boa tied around her neck.

Fannie Mae always told Belle, "Don't you let them make no sideshow out of my funeral." Then she would laugh out loud at the very thought of it. "That boy is just too funny," she would add to Belle.

CHAPTER 3

QUIET PLEASE! (THE MICE ARE PISSING ON COTTON)

After kissing her mother's cold forehead, Belle ran her fingers along the edges of Fannie Mae's quilt, smoothing it out over her body to make her appear as if she was just sleeping. Belle pulled a chair beside her mother's bed. She began the task of mentally planning what steps to take next in notifying the proper authorities, her sisters and Pastor Hicks. There would be time for crying later. She wanted to keep herself together in order to make the necessary telephone calls. Belle knew that calling her sisters would be the most daunting and difficult task of all — especially Lena Turner. She just wasn't ready for a performance by this dramatic actress. She would definitely save her for last.

Belle decided to call Pastor Hicks first. "Hello Pastor Hicks, my mama done died in her sleep. Mama done gone home to the Lord," Belle continued.

"Me and Mrs. Hicks are going to come by directly," he replied and hung up the telephone before Belle could ask him what to do next.

Next she dialed 911. "My mama done died on me!" Belle said when the 911 operator came on the line.

"I'm so sorry, we will send someone right away," the operator said.

In Macon County, everyone knew everybody — and everyone knew Miss Fannie Mae Turner. She was one of the most beloved citizens in the county. Persons of all races and from all walks of life loved her. That was a rarity in Oglethorpe, Georgia. It was the kind of place where everybody had something bad to say about somebody, but this was not the case when it came to Miss Fannie Mae.

"Sis, you and Joe Bamo get on over here quick, Mama done died," Belle told her sister Nettie.

"What done happened?" Nettie asked with extreme calmness.

"Never you mind what done happened, just get on over here," Belle replied.

"We is a coming," replied Nettie in a quiet tone.

Nettie was the quietest and the most shy of Henry and Fannie Mae Turner's daughters. She and her husband, Joe Bamo, lived only a few minutes away from the home place. They lived over on Oglethorpe Road across from the local cemetery, which was segregated and divided between blacks and whites. The graves of the white families were on the front side of the cemetery, with the blacks buried way in the back far from the road.

Nettie and Joe Bamo, who was equally as quiet and shy as his wife, would sit on their front porch and watch the burials of the white folks taking place. They had to go to an upstairs window and crane their necks whenever there was a black burial happening way at the back of the cemetery. Most of their ancestors were buried there in the old cemetery.

Nettie and Joe enjoyed fishing together and watching funerals — that was about all they did except for Sunday dinners at Fannie Mae's before she became too ill to cook. When there was no funeral happening across the road, Nettie and Joe just rocked back and forth in their rocking chairs, watching cars go by on Oglethorpe Road. There was rarely a word passed between them.

Nettie and Joe had the most to say when they went to church on Sundays and to supper at Fannie Mae's house. "How do Pastor Hicks?" Nettie or Joe interchangeably might ask, or, "How do Mrs. Hicks?" or, "How do Deacon Smalls?" and so on and so on.

They sat quietly in church with barely an "amen" uttered. It was painful for most of the other churchgoers to watch them sit there so quietly. After all, Pastor Hicks was all fire and brimstone, and Nettie and Joe were as quiet as "mice pissin' on cotton." When they got to Fannie Mae's house for Sunday supper, they would sit side-by-side together on the front porch swing, swaying back and forth without saying a word until it was time to eat.

"Nice supper, Mama." Nettie would also say.

"Nice supper, Mrs. Turner," Joe Bamo would add in.

After supper they would both say, "Thank you, I guess we

ought to be going now. See you next Sunday."

They were the same way whether it was family or total strangers.

~

Now, Nettie and Joe Bamo faced another funeral at the back of the cemetery on Oglethorpe Road. This time they would be up close and personal instead of watching from their upstairs window. They would be saying their final "goodbyes."

"Goodbye, Mama," Nettie would probably say quietly.

"Goodbye, Mrs. Turner," Joe Bamo would say just as quietly.

After the burial, they would go back to the church for the repast. The Bamos would sit side-by-side together with their heads hung low and just nod "thank you" to all those who bothered to offer their condolences.

Nettie and Joe Bamo's lives would still remain forever quiet and yet would be forever changed. They would miss and mourn Miss Fannie Mae by retreating into their own little world of silence. Theirs was a world where most strangers were hardly ever invited in and seldom welcome.

Next on Belle's list to call was her sister Rosalie who lived down in Albany, Georgia with her husband, Esau, and their very delicate son, Marshall. Rose was the loudest of all of the Turner sisters. When the Tate family used to arrive for supper on the third Sunday of each month before Fannie Mae took sick, first you heard the car then you heard "Big Red."

"Mama, we is here!" she would shout at the top of her lungs as soon as she got out of backseat of Esau's old Buick with the rusty chrome bumpers. She would be on the front porch of

Fannie Mae's house before Esau and Marshall could even get out of the car's front seat.

"Sis, Joe Bamo, what you two fools doing sitting out here like two bumps on a log?" she would bellow out, causing them to tremble and shake to their very cores. Their peace and quiet was shattered completely whenever Rosalie came to visit.

"Mama, is dinner ready yet? What you cooking? I bet you we having chicken and dressing!" she would yell from the parlor to the kitchen.

Fannie Mae would simply reply, "Yes, Sugar, chicken and dressing."

"Big Red" would take her same seat as always in the recliner that was her daddy, Henry's. She would take off her red patent-leather high heels that were two sizes too small, wiggle her toes inside of her pantyhose, and cry out, "Ooh child, them shoes are killing my corns and bunions!"

She wore those same red shoes every third Sunday of the month without fail. And, she would have the same complaints about them.

Nobody could get a word in edge-wise when "Big Red" started to talk. She never missed telling poor Esau, "Look what you got! Ain't you just damn lucky?"

Rosalie was about four-inches taller than Esau and about 50-pounds heavier. He did not dare to cross her when she was all fired up. Marshall, on the other hand, would go toe-to-toe with his mother. He would show her the back of his hand or snap his fingers in the air in a wide circle when he wanted to get her attention.

Marshall would say to his mother, "You need to step back Miss Joan Crawford, you're standing in my light." Or with his hands on his hips, "Miss Thing, I'll read you from Genesis to Revelations!"

Rosalie just grinned and gave Marshall the floor. They were like two pole beans in the same pod — you could hardly tell them apart. Marshall and his mother were just like twin sisters. He wore red patent leather slip-ons with white top stitching to match his mother's shoes. Yes, every third Sunday that is what they wore! Marshall also wore a matching red scarf tied loosely and billowing about his neck.

Fannie Mae just shook her head and told Rosalie and Marshall, "You all behave when Pastor and Mrs. Hicks get here. I don't want any of your foolishness!"

When Belle called the Tate house, Esau answered the telephone. "Esau, where's Rosalie?"

"She's still sleeping," he answered.

"Well then, tell her to wake up! Mama is dead! Mama is dead!" Belle cried.

"I don't know if I should wake her yet, she likes to sleep late on account of today is New Year's Day."

Belle lost her patience and demanded that Esau wake his wife.

He timidly approached the bedroom door with the cordless phone in hand. He tapped at the door lightly then stuck his head inside. "Rosalie, you awake?"

Rosalie turned over and growled at Esau, "What you want fool?"

"It's Belle on the phone, she says your mama is dead," he murmured.

She shot straight up in bed and snatched the cordless phone from Esau's hand. "What you mean Mama's dead?" she shouted into the phone.

Belle's ears were ringing from the loud, piercing sound of Rosalie's voice and the heaving, sobbing and crying that followed.

When Rosalie regained her composure, she told Belle that she, Esau and Marshall would drive up from Albany right away.

On the other hand, Belle was hoping that they would take their sweet time. She was in no mood for "Big Red" and Marshall, at least not at this moment. Her brother-in-law Esau was never a problem, but Rosalie and Marshall were drama queens who would make things just plain downright unbearable and complicated.

But what Belle really dreaded was the eventual arrival of the real actress in the family, Elenora "Girlie" Lena Turner. She did not have to worry about it too soon, as it was a long bus ride back from New York City. So, Belle cleverly made sure that she was the last on the call list.

Her next call would be to Christine "Sweetie Pie" up in Atlanta. She could get her shady boyfriend, Horace Lee, to drive her the two hours down from Atlanta. They had matching gold front teeth and his and hers Jheri-curls. Rosalie and Marshall referred to them as the "Gold Dust Twins" or "Mr. and Mrs. Worry Curl." There was also usually some reference made about Eddie Murphy's "Classy Curl" commercial skit on "Saturday Night Live" where curl activator spews from his hair like lava from an erupting volcano.

Rosalie and Marshall were inappropriate on so many levels. They always spoke what was on their minds, which was usually the truth. The mother and son were like a wrestling tag team. One would distract their opponent while the other would sucker punch with sarcastic and acerbic wit. There was no match for the terrible twosome from Albany, Georgia.

When Belle telephoned Christine to tell her of their mother's death, Christine searched for just the right words to say to console the sister who had been closest to their mother in her later years. Christine was the queen of malapropisms. Since moving up to Atlanta from Macon County, she always tried to use "big" words to impress her relatives who were still stuck down in the country, way back up in the woods. She almost always used words that she had heard or read, but did not know the meaning of. Often she used non-words like "conversate" or "irregardless." The people who knew her best somehow always knew what she was trying to say, even when she was being uppity.

"Oh Belle, you must be just 'desecrated' by Mama's 'despise,'" which translated to "devastated by Mama's demise." "You and Mama 'conversated' almost every day. You must be feeling so 'sadly.' I know that you are going to miss her matter of 'factly.' I will miss her truthfully too! Did you say Mama died of 'cardio arrest?'" Christine asked.

Christine then told Belle that she would head down to Oglethorpe just as soon as she could get Horace Lee out of bed.

"That man just wants to be on top of me all day long!" Christine complained. That was the last thing that Belle wanted to hear. Christine was always putting her business out in the street.

The night before, Christine and Horace Lee had made their way over to Bigelow's on Gresham Road just off of I-20 East in Atlanta to ring in the New Year. Although Atlanta has its share of upscale clubs, Bigelow's Bar and Grill is the place to be for a truly ethnic, Afro-centric experience. Even some of the most cultured, educated and affluent black folks in Atlanta find their way back to Bigelow's for a late-night snack of fried chicken, shrimp or fish in a basket.

On New Year's Eve, Christine and Horace Lee wore matching black and shiny gold outfits. Christine had on black jeans with gold stripes so tight that she had two muffin tops spilling over the top of her waist band between the jeans and her black-and-gold sequined top, accented by gold patent-leather ankle boots and a gold counterfeit Gucci handbag. Horace Lee wore a three-piece black suit with wide chalk stripes in bright gold on the wide-pleated pants, and a gold vest and jacket that came down to his calves. His shirt was gold satin with ruffles and opened down to the top button of his vest to reveal his three gold-plated chains and medallion.

Needless to say, they were just too fine for words — gold teeth and all. Christine and Horace Lee were just one hot mess! Christine thought that she and Horace Lee might one day qualify to be on "The Real Housewives of Atlanta," the reality television show that exemplifies and glorifies the height of tackiness and gaudiness. The television show and its inhabitants are an embarrassment to real people of substance in Atlanta.

Belle made the final telephone call to her baby sister Elenora. The hotel desk clerk in New York told Belle, "We have a Lena Turner in room 19, but no Elenora."

Belle confirmed for him that they were one and the same. He said that he would slip a note under her door since there were no telephones in the rooms. There was only a pay phone down the hall near the bathrooms. Belle found this odd since Elenora always bragged about her fancy hotel suite just off Broadway. She was way off Broadway and perhaps a little crazy as well! She was never the same after she left Oglethorpe, Georgia as a teenager.

Lena Turner surely would be sleeping in late on New Year's Day. She probably had a hangover from cheap gin, Cold Duck, and too many Camel cigarettes that she chain smoked all day long.

Elenora called Belle back at about 6:00 p.m. that evening. She showed absolutely no emotion when told about her mother's death. This took Belle by surprise, because Elenora was always in theatrical mode.

Her only response was, "Can you buy me a Greyhound bus ticket back home to Oglethorpe? I'll pay you back just as soon as I get an advance from my next show opening in about three weeks." She always had a new show or some singing engagement opening in about three weeks!

Belle simply said, "Whatever! I'll take care of your ticket tomorrow. Roundtrip I hope!"

"Thanks, Lil Buck," Girlie said. "Make sure that you use

my right name, Lena Turner, that's LENA, just like in Lena Horne!"

It would be a tedious and difficult journey without being able to smoke on the long bus ride back to Georgia. She would have to stock up on some Nicorette gum to get through the trip.

Belle braced herself for what was to come. She had stayed close to her mother ever since her father, Henry, died in 1992 and even closer when her mother took ill. She cared for her right up until the end. Even though Nettie and her husband, Joe Bamo, lived close by, they only showed up for dinner on Sundays after church. Nettie was so quiet she would not have been good company for Fannie Mae anyway.

Rosalie down in Albany had her hands full just keeping control over her husband, Esau, and keeping her son, Marshall, from bringing strange men into their home after she went to bed. Marshall had been arrested several times for soliciting men in the center of town in Albany, Georgia. He was notorious for offering sex to any man on the street who would listen. Rosalie feared for her safety should Marshall bring home a serial killer or axe murderer. She would stay awake at night until Marshall was in his bed and all alone.

A light was left on in her bedroom, signaling that she was up and watching his every move. Poor Esau could not sleep because of the light that was constantly shining in his eyes. Rosalie caught Marshall once bringing a stranger into their home — and that was all that it took. She met them at the door with a cast-iron frying pan in her hand. Marshall's trick took off running down the street and never looked back.

She snatched Marshall in the collar and told him, "I'll beat your little, narrow black ass into next week. I brought you into this world, and I'll take you out! Don't mess with Big Red!"

He knew that Rosalie meant what she said.

Christine and Elenora were both in their own little worlds of delusions of grandeur and mistaken identity. They hardly had time to even call Fannie Mae, given their fast-paced lives in Atlanta and New York City respectively. But, their mother loved them just the same. All of Fannie Mae's daughters were equal in her eyes and in her heart.

Belle was the only one who Fannie Mae could really depend on. She kept her company when she was lonely. She helped her to cook and clean when she was too tired. She read to her when her eyes were weak. Belle was Fannie Mae's all-around companion after Henry Turner died. She drove Fannie Mae to church service on Sundays and to Bible study on Wednesday nights. Belle did the grocery shopping for her mother. She was a lifeline for Fannie Mae and her connection to the outside world. In many ways Belle "Lil Buck" Turner became her mother's guardian. In the latter years, she was the replacement for Fannie Mae's daddy, Buck Jessup, who she lost so very long ago to the KKK.

CHAPTER 4

PASTOR HICKS AND FAT ETHEL (THE MAD HATTER)

The 911 operator Gertie Matthews notified the Oglethorpe Police Department, who in turn contacted the Macon County Coroner's Office to advise them that Miss Fannie Mae Turner had died in her home. Gertie Matthews was born Gertrude English. Her family, descendants of Sampson J. English, had resided in Macon County since the early 1830s. The English family name had been prominent in the county ever since. The branches of the family had spread far and wide over and around this region of the Flint River in South Georgia. Throughout history, the English family had united in marriage with many other families in the area. It was hard to find a family that was not somehow related to the English family, including some blacks.

Gertie was known for her patient, calm and compassionate manner when handling emergency and non-emergency calls, such as: 'Can you send someone to get my cat down from the tree? She always complied with concern and compassion. Gertie considered the needs of all citizens of Macon County to be important, whether they be rich or poor, black or white. It was her civic duty, and she carried it out with pride.

Pastor Rogers Hicks and his wife, Ethel, arrived at Fannie Mae's house just before Oglethorpe police officer John Henry Johnson showed up. There was time for Pastor Hicks to say a prayer over Fannie Mae's body and to console Belle and prepare her for the questions that she would have to answer regarding finding her mother's dead body. Ethel Hicks had a very comforting demeanor. She held Belle's hand while Pastor Hicks talked to Belle about whether to have her mother's funeral at the church or at Meadows Oglethorpe Funeral Chapel.

The Meadows family had been handling the funeral needs of families in Macon County, Georgia and the surrounding areas since 1957. Since Fannie Mae's parents were founding members of the New Ebenezer First Missionary Baptist Church to which she belonged since birth, it would only be proper and fitting that her services be held there. Meadows would handle the arrangements. The Meadows family members were distant relatives of many of the families that they prepared for homegoing services. They were known for their reputation as the best in comfort and care for grieving families, not only in Macon County, but also at their chapel in Atlanta.

Ethel Hicks was also known for her nurturing compassion in times of need. She was known affectionately as "Fat Ethel" ever since she was a little girl. Once she became the Pastor's wife only her family and closest friends called her that in private and never in public. Ethel Hicks loved her hats. She special ordered her hats from a hat maker in Philadelphia, Pennsylvania where her sister Thelma lived. She would never buy hats locally for fear that one of her church members would show up with the same one on. She had a hat and shoes to match every Sunday outfit in her closet — hats for funerals, christenings, baptisms and weddings.

Because of her size, she custom ordered her clothes and shoes from a store in Atlanta where her other sister Doris Sherard lived. Her sister Doris was a matron of black society in Atlanta. She played bridge twice a week and hosted charity teas and luncheons to benefit the disadvantaged and disaffected. Doris was the epitome of a black southern belle. Words flowed from her lips like sweet molasses dripping from a spigot. She shopped exclusively at Saks Fifth Avenue and Neiman Marcus in Atlanta. Doris Sherard had integrated the finest stores and shops in Atlanta even before there was a law telling her that she could do so. No mere store clerk would ever refuse her or deny her the right to shop. Ethel Hicks, like her sister Doris in Atlanta, was her own one-of-a-kind woman in Oglethorpe, Georgia with her one-of-a-kind fashions.

In contrast to his wife, Pastor Hicks was tall and thin with horn-rimmed eyeglasses and a long neck. He was all legs and no torso. When he walked alongside his loving wife, "Fat Ethel," it was like Melman the giraffe and Gloria the hippopotamus in "Madagascar 2." He was tall and hyper; she was short, plump and calm. He was light-skinned with pockmarks on his face from childhood acne; she had a smooth complexion, the color of golden, sweet honey.

They were opposites who were truly attracted to one another and fell in love. He always felt that she was a gift from God. They met shortly after he finished Divinity School in Atlanta and became an ordained Baptist minister. He had prayed that one day he would return to Oglethorpe, Georgia, find a wife, and become the pastor of his own church. God evidently heard his prayers and granted all three. He became an associate pastor at New Ebenezer First Missionary Baptist Church, and then ascended to the first chair when Pastor Ezekiel Caldwell retired.

Pastor Hicks was pacing the floor with his hands clasped behind his back. Mrs. Hicks sat next to Belle on the flower-print sofa, holding her hand while officer John Henry Johnson, who was seated in Henry Turner's old recliner, questioned her about the circumstances leading up to finding her mother's body that morning. John Henry knew the Turner family well. He, his sisters Patricia and Joan, and his brothers, the twins Purvis and Percival, had attended school with the Turner girls. He was the first boy to make it all the way with the fast-and-frisky Elenora "Girlie" Turner. He was Porgy to her Bess. It was summertime and the living was easy. She was Carmen Jones to his Joe. Dorothy Dandridge was her other favorite light-skinned black actress along with Lena Horne. John Henry Johnson had Harry Belafonte-like features.

He was known around Macon County, Georgia as a "pretty boy." All the girls wanted a piece of John Henry, but Elenora wanted it all. And, she was willing to give it all. Word around Oglethorpe was that John Henry was actually named after Henry Turner, and that he bore an uncanny resemblance to his namesake. It was quite possible that he and Elenora Turner were half-siblings. Henry tried to keep a close eye on his youngest daughter whenever John Henry Johnson came to call. He tried everything he could to keep them from getting into trouble. The consequences would be devastating for both of their families.

"What time did you get here to your mama's house?" John Henry asked Belle.

"About the same time that I get here every morning, 'bout 7:30," Belle replied.

"What time did you find your mama dead?"

"I don't generally wake her until I get her breakfast cooked, about 8:15 I reckon."

"I went in her room, and she was sleeping so peacefully, just like an angel. I didn't want to bother her, but Mama wants to eat when she wants to eat. I took and shook and shook, then I felt her hand, it was cold like ice. That's when I knew she was dead."

"What did you do then?" John Henry asked.

"I called Pastor Hicks and told him that my mama done died in her sleep. She done gone home to the Lord!"

That was all that John Henry needed to know. There was no indication that there was any foul play. The coroner would determine the actual cause of death, most likely a natural death brought on by the fact that Fannie Mae Turner was just tired, old and weak. This was all just routine procedure. The death of Fannie Mae Turner was treated like any other death in Macon County, Georgia.

Fannie Mae's body was transported to Meadows Oglethorpe Funeral Chapel for the start of her home-going preparation. Belle stood on the front porch waving "goodbye" to her mama while holding the folded quilt that had covered her mother's body. She was thinking that her mother would be reunited with her husband, Henry, and the many relatives and friends who had preceded her in death, which reminded Belle that she would have to get funeral programs to the many friends and neighbors who now lived in nearby nursing homes: Senior Care in Montezuma, Magnolia Manor in Ideal, and The Oaks in Marshallville.

Belle had not even noticed when Nettie and Joe Bamo arrived, but her silent thoughts and reflections were shattered when she heard her sister Rosalie in the front yard yell, "Belle, I'm here, where's my mama?"

Her husband and son, Marshall, who wore a bright-yellow flowing scarf tied loosely and fluffily around his neck, trailed Rosalie. Marshall's scarf matched the color of Rosalie's blouse with a ruffled neckline. Even though it was January, Marshall and Rosalie both looked like Big Bird on Easter Sunday. The two of them were the most flamboyant mother and son in all of Albany, Georgia. Wherever they went people were sure to notice them. People would just stop and stare with their mouths wide open. Whenever they shopped at the Piggly Wiggly supermarket, the other shoppers found it hard to concentrate. They were so completely in awe and distracted by Rosalie and Marshall Tate. Other shoppers would just follow them up and down the aisles of the supermarket just to catch another glimpse of the odd pair. Rosalie always wore a big bow on the back of her hair that was color coordinated with whatever clothing she was wearing and Marshall matched his mother. If she wore lavender, he wore a lavender scarf. If she wore pink, he wore a pink scarf. If she wore chartreuse, his scarf was the same color. Marshall had a scarf for every outfit in his mother's closet. They both wore pastel eye shadow in the same shade as their clothing and accessories.

Poor Esau Tate was so embarrassed by the attention that his wife and son attracted. When he took them shopping, he would wait in the car until they finished. Marshall Tate started mimicking his mother when he was about five years old. Rosalie was flattered by his antics since she had always wanted to have a little girl. And, she was the boss in the Tate household. Esau also never tried to stop his son's growing interest in all things feminine and that made Rosalie encourage Marshall's behavior even more.

There the three of them stood in Fannie Mae's front yard while Belle, Nettie and Joe Bamo stood on the porch. Belle just shook her head. While she was saddened by the death of her mother, she found Rosalie and Marshall simply amusing. She did everything in her power to stifle the laugh that was trying to find its way out of her throat. The bright yellow mess standing before them amused even Nettie and Joe Bamo. Nettie had the same shy smile that Whoopi Goldberg had when she played Miss Celie in "The Color Purple," and Joe Bamo was much like the quiet Harpo.

"Belle, where is my mama?" Rosalie repeated.

"You all come on inside. It's cold out here," Belle replied.

"I want to know where my mama is," Rosalie yelled again impatiently.

"Come on inside, and I'll tell you," replied Belle in a reassuring voice.

Belle, Nettie and Joe Bamo went inside Fannie Mae's house followed by Rosalie, Esau and Marshall. Rosalie never stopped talking from the front yard all the way to the living room. After getting inside of the house, she and Marshall had intermittent bouts of grief.

There were wails coming from Rosalie, "Mama, why did you leave me? Mama, why did you have to go so soon?"

And, from Marshall came, "Mama Girl, I need you. Mama Girl, how am I going to make it without you?"

They always made everything about them. No one else ever seemed to matter.

Belle told everyone that when she found Fannie Mae's body, she looked just like an angel sleeping. She said that she had a sweet smile on her face, and that she went quietly in her sleep. She told them that Fannie Mae's death was painless and swift. Belle was only speculating that her mother did not suffer. She had no idea of the fright that her mother experienced just before she died; however, she wondered if the gunshots that she heard on New Year's Eve caused her mother any anxiety or stress.

Belle had to be the calm voice of comfort and reason for the rest of the family, especially Rosalie. Rosalie and her son Marshall were prone to spontaneous outbursts of emotions no matter what the situation or what they were told. Belle, while feeling sorrow at the loss of her beloved mother, Fannie Mae, felt empathy for poor Esau Tate for having to live in the same house with Rosalie and Marshall. They were absolutely unbearable. He was always put upon and outnumbered by his wife and son. Esau Tate was not the ruler in his own castle. He was more like a servant to an imperialistic queen and a despot prince. He chauffeured them wherever they wanted to go and waited endlessly for them to finish whatever business they were doing. Esau abided by their wishes and never complained.

Belle told Rosalie, Esau, Marshall, Nettie and Joe Bamo that Fannie Mae's body had been transported over to Meadows Oglethorpe Funeral Chapel for preparation. She told them that once Christine and Elenora arrived in Oglethorpe, the whole family would go over to Meadows together to preview Fannie Mae's body. Until then, the rest of the family would just have to relax and make themselves at home in Fannie Mae's house. She would have wanted it that way.

CHAPTER 5

STEP ABOARD, THIS BUS IS HEADING SOUTH

Elenora "Girlie" Turner (aka Lena Turner) had not set foot back in Macon County since her daddy, Henry, died back in 1992. She dreaded having to return for her mother Fannie Mae's funeral. There were just too many painful memories of her childhood growing up poor on a farm at the end of a dusty dirt road in Oglethorpe, Georgia. She had become an accomplished actress, singer and dancer in New York City, at least in the theater of her own mind. She was truthfully nearly homeless, living in a fleabag hotel room with a two-burner hotplate for cooking, a pay phone, and shared bathroom facilities down the hall. Her neighbors were drug dealers, pimps, prostitutes and other welfare recipients like herself.

She would have to endure the nearly 1,000-mile bus ride from New York to Macon, Georgia, the nearest bus station to

Oglethorpe. The trip would take approximately 24 hours. Then she would have to suffer a 60-mile car ride from Macon to Oglethorpe in complete and total silence with her sister Nettie and Nettie's husband, Joe Bamo, who rarely uttered a word. The other option would be getting a ride from her sister Rosalie, Rosalie's husband, Esau, and their near-drag-queen son, Marshall. Neither option appealed to Lena Turner; but she would much rather suffer in silence than listen to "Big Red's" big mouth and Marshall's lisp and whiny, effeminate voice! Living in New York, she was surrounded by loud, pushy women like her sister Rosalie and screaming queens like her nephew. She expected that kind of behavior in the big city, but not in South Georgia.

Lena stuffed her large, soft-sided plaid suitcase with vintage 1950s glamour ensembles that she had collected over the years from thrift stores. The clothes allowed her to live in her fantasy world of Dorothy Dandridge, Lena Horne and Lana Turner. She certainly attracted attention on the streets of New York in her cinched-waist dresses, swing coats, pencil skirts, clutch bags, open-toed mules and sling-back shoes. The higher the shoe was the better to show off her shapely legs. If she had a television set with cable in her room, she would definitely be a fan of AMC's "Madmen," where the women prance around in the same fashion with cigarettes dangling between their fingers.

She would no doubt be the star at Fannie Mae's funeral. She cringed to think of how many times she would have to correct people who called her "Elenora" or "Girlie!" "My name is Lena Turner, L-E-N-A, just like Lena Horne!" she would correct them. She imagined that people would come from miles around just to get a look at her. It would be like a Broadway opening once they found out that Lena Turner was back in town! All of the girls who had hated her in high school and all of the boys who had wanted her would attend Fannie Mae Turner's funeral to pay tribute to the one who got away from Macon County, Georgia.

She had already begun practicing her entrance into the sanctuary at New Ebenezer First Missionary Baptist Church. The congregation gathered for her mother's home-going service would be standing and awaiting her arrival. They would all sit down once she was seated in the family pew. She smiled at the thought.

Christine and Horace Lee only had to take a short two-hour drive down from Atlanta. They had to prepare for at least a few days down in the country, in the backwoods of South Georgia. Horace Lee Miller was from Ellaville, Georgia in Schley (pronounced Sly) County, the next county over from Macon County where Christine Turner was from. They first met in Atlanta at Bigelow's Bar and Grill. They were completely surprised to find out that they grew up so close to one another yet had never met. Horace Lee intended to visit his family in Ellaville while attending Miss Fannie Mae's funeral.

Horace Lee loaded Christine's set of counterfeit Louis Vuitton luggage into the trunk of his 1979 Chrysler Cordoba, which was dark maroon with a padded roof and "soft Corinthian leather." Her fake Louis Vuitton luggage set was a Christmas gift that Horace Lee picked up from a Korean vendor at

The Mall West End in Atlanta. They were dressed in matching polyester tracksuits and tennis shoes in dark maroon to match the Cordoba for their trip home to South Georgia. They packed in the luggage additional matching outfits to last them for a whole week. Rosalie and Marshall would have themselves a field day when they caught sight of the "Gold Dust Twins" with Jheri-curled hair pulling into Fannie Mae's front yard. At least it would help them to forget their grief for a moment.

Belle had asked Christine if she and Horace Lee could give Elenora a ride from Atlanta if she got off the bus there from New York. Christine did not respond. She did not trust her flirtatious younger sister around her man. She would be watching Horace Lee's roaming eyes and hands as well. She had caught him cheating and lying more than once in the past. There was one time that she walked up on Horace Lee and another woman at Bigelow's Bar and Grill. Before the other woman knew what had happened, Christine had knocked her from her barstool. Horace Lee ran out the door, leaving his companion stunned and spread out on the floor with Christine standing over her. The woman dared not get up. When Christine caught up with Horace Lee, he was crouched down in the backseat of his car. He did not want the same punishment as Christine had dealt to the other woman. His punishment was no sex for a month. He never set foot in Bigelow's again without Christine on his arm. He loved sex too much to do without it.

Often times, Fannie Mae Turner spoke to Belle, Nettie and Joe Bamo about her wishes when the day came for her "to leave this wicked Earth." She tried to have the same conversation on the third Sundays of the month when Rosalie, Esau and

Marshall used to come for supper, but Rosalie and Marshall would never let Fannie Mae have her say.

Rosalie would interrupt, "Oh, Mama don't you talk such nonsense. God don't want you yet!"

Then Marshall would chime in with his shrill voice, "Mama Girl, you and me too pretty to die! God takes the ugly ones first. It'll be a while before he gets around to us! Now you just put a period on that sentence and hush up."

The conversation about death and dying would end abruptly. Fannie Mae Turner did not want such foolish talk on the Lord's Day. However, she did share her dreams for a proper funeral and burial with the ones who counted: Belle, Pastor Hicks and his wife, Ethel. She knew that her wishes would be carried out to the letter as long as those three had a say in making her final arrangements.

During one of Fannie Mae's funeral conversations with Pastor and Mrs. Hicks, Ethel Hicks shared her plans for her own perfect funeral whenever the time should come. She had attended the funeral of a distant relative in Philadelphia, Margaret Elizabeth Trusty. Like Ethel Hicks, Mrs. Trusty loved her hats and was the best-dressed woman in her church all the way up until she died at the age of 94. She was beautiful and stylish to the very end. At her funeral, her collection of hats was displayed on head forms in every window throughout the sanctuary, and the floral arrangement on her casket had one of her favorite hats as the centerpiece.

It was the most beautiful funeral that Ethel Hicks had ever attended. She told her husband, Pastor Hicks, and Miss

Fannie Mae that she wanted a funeral just like Margaret Trusty's — she wanted her hats displayed all over the sanctuary of New Ebenezer First Missionary Baptist Church. Just like Margaret Trusty could count on her granddaughter Robin Hammond to carry out her final plans, Fannie Mae Turner knew that her daughter Belle would do the same.

Fannie Mae's chosen colors for her funeral were white and heavenly blue. White was for the angels who would be sent to greet her and heavenly blue was the color of her eternal resting place. She envisioned her casket in the prettiest shade of blue with white-satin lining. The church sanctuary would be festooned with blue-and-white floral arrangements. There would be white roses, lilies and orchids, blue hydrangeas, hyacinths and delphiniums — these were all her favorite flowers. She would be dressed in a gown of baby blue with a white sash around her waist. Blue slippers and her cultured pearl earrings, necklace and bracelet would add the perfect touch.

She also imagined white funeral cars for transporting her and her family to Oglethorpe Cemetery where at the conclusion of the graveside dedication of her body, white doves would be released to carry her spirit home. Fannie Mae Turner would be laid to rest next to her beloved Henry and near the graves of her mother, Jesse, and her three boys who died at childbirth. She would be near the marker left for her father, Buck, whose body was never found after the Ku Klux Klan took him away so many years before. She wanted her five daughters dressed in white and her two sons-in-law in blue. Her grandson, Marshall, would probably opt for wearing white with a blue chiffon neck scarf tied in a big fluffy bow. She had always chuckled at the thought!

Fannie Mae did not care much for the fact that Christine lived in sin up in Atlanta with that Horace Lee Miller. Nor, did she care what color he would wear to her funeral. More than likely, he would wear his white pimp suit and white derby hat to match Christine, seeing as how they always dressed alike. She had seen that "get up" in pictures that Christine had sent to Belle.

Ethel Hicks would handle the duty of reading cards and acknowledgements. She hoped that Ethel would choose to wear her powder-blue coatdress with matching hat, shoes and handbag. Her funeral would be set right down to the very last detail thanks to Belle, Pastor Hicks and his wife. All the others had to do was just show up.

Fannie Mae reminded Rosalie and Marshall more than once that, "God will be watching, so don't you two cut the fool! I don't want no crying and bawling over me when I'm lying in that there casket."

She did not have to worry about Nettie and Joe Bamo. They hardly ever made a peep anyway. Christine would be too busy keeping her eye on Horace Lee. And, Elenora "Girlie" Lena Turner would save her best acting for the repast back at the church hall.

Belle would be the matriarch of the Turner family now that Fannie Mae went home to rest. She would keep the others in line after her mother's death. She was like her granddaddy Buck through and through and would not stand for any foolishness!

"Lil Buck" would remind "Sis," "Big Red," "Sweetie Pie" and "Girlie" who was boss. Since she was the oldest of the Turner sisters, her parents counted on Belle to set a good example for the others. She learned to cook from her mother and passed whatever she learned in the kitchen down to her younger sisters. The lessons that she learned from both of her parents allowed her to step in whenever either of them didn't feel well, or if they were away and she was in charge.

Even though Fannie Mae had only vague memories of her father, Buck, before he left the home place mysteriously that night when she was only five years old, she always saw his traits and characteristics in her daughter Belle. She went by what she had been told about him. Fannie Mae never had any siblings of her own, and her mother, Jesse, never remarried after her father was declared missing and presumed dead.

She did not know what it was really like to have a man around the house until she married Henry Turner, but it seemed that somehow her father's spirit had jumped right over her and into the body of her daughter Belle. At times, Belle could be like both a father and a mother to her younger sisters. Fannie Mae could rest in peace eternally knowing that Belle was in charge. The younger sisters always treated her with respect as if she was a third parent. This dynamic had never changed in the Turner family and would continue long after Fannie Mae's death.

CHAPTER 6

THE GATHERING OF THE FLOCK (AT THE HOME PLACE)

Rosalie, Esau and Marshall Tate had arrived from Albany to Fannie Mae's house in Oglethorpe in the early afternoon on New Year's Day. They had arrived just after Nettie and Joe Bamo who lived nearby. Rather than drive back and forth to Albany, they came prepared to stay until after the funeral. Rosalie and Marshall had two suitcases apiece while Esau only had one. Rosalie and her son wanted to be ready for any occasion. In the dead of winter, they had brought their finest spring clothing in the brightest pastel colors. They could stay in Fannie Mae's home or in the two spare bedrooms in Belle's house just through the clearing in the woods. This would all be settled once everyone else had arrived.

Belle secretly hoped that Rosalie and Marshall would split up for the evening or decide to stay at Fannie Mae's. She could not take both of them if they decided to stay at her house. Her brother-in-law Esau was her favorite to have as a house-guest. Her sister and her nephew would completely shatter the peace and solitude that she had become accustomed to.

Christine Turner and Horace Lee Miller did not arrive from Atlanta until the next morning. Nettie and Joe Bamo, who lived nearby, were already at the house waiting with Belle and the Tates for their arrival. When Christine and Horace Lee walked into the house, the others were all sitting down to eat breakfast. Belle, in anticipation of their arrival, prepared plenty of food. There they were — the four older Turner girls, Belle, Nettie, Rosalie and Christine once again eating at Fannie Mae's table.

Horace Lee greeted the whole family and offered his condolences. He shook hands with Esau and Joe Bamo. He hugged Belle, Nettie and Rosalie. He did not know exactly what to do with Marshall. Should he hug him or shake his hand? So, he did neither. Christine and Horace Lee both sat down at the big kitchen table for a country-style breakfast. Each time they took a bite, their gold teeth sparkled and flashed in the light. Nettie and Joe Bamo were so bashful they lowered their heads. They did not want to get caught staring at the flashy dental work.

Marshall kept looking at his mother, Rosalie, to call her attention to the twin Jheri-curls. Esau just sat there watching his wife and son. The two of them did not care if they were seen misbehaving. Belle tried to ignore them all.

"I wish that I could have been here with you when you found Mama," Christine offered. "I am so sorry that you had to be all alone at such an awful time," she continued. "Are you sure that it was 'cardio-arrest?'"

Marshall and Rosalie just looked at one another, and Belle pretended not to even hear Christine's question. This was no time to be embarrassed by her misuse of common language.

At about 1:30 in the afternoon Nettie and Joe Bamo were ready to head up to Macon to meet Elenora's bus coming in from New York. Rosalie, Esau and Marshall offered to go instead. But, Nettie and Joe Bamo just wanted to get away from the noise that had already started to develop around them.

Christine was in her non-stop mode of misusing words. She was a card-carrying member of the "NWCP" chapter in Atlanta. She had a "41K" plan at work. She liked the "Rotisary" chicken from Publix rather than from Kroger. She preferred "Napoleon" ice cream instead of plain vanilla, chocolate or strawberry. She liked the way all three flavors were mixed together. She gets "flusterated" when people don't understand her. She wished that she had time to finish her undergraduate and master's degrees, and then go for her "doctrine." She and Horace Lee had "woked up" early this morning so that they could drive down to Macon County. She went on and on.

Rosalie and Marshall would not stop talking about how people all over Albany were just plain jealous of their style and fashion sense. They talked about how people would just stop and stare at them whenever they went to the Piggly Wiggly, bank or mall.

Nettie and Joe Bamo lived such a quiet existence that this gathering of relatives was far too traumatic for them. The peace and quiet at least for the ride to Macon would do them both some good. The return ride back from Macon with Elenora "Girlie" Lena Turner in tow would be another matter. Knowing they were both shy and quiet, she would still try to force them both to talk about things in Oglethorpe — people, places and, of course, Fannie Mae's final days. They suffered through the hour-plus ride back to the home place. For the first time in his life, Joe Bamo risked getting a speeding ticket just to hurry the trip along.

When Lena Turner stepped off the Greyhound bus at 2:45 p.m. in Macon, Georgia, she was dressed in leopard-print slacks with a faux leopard swing coat and hat, and black suede ankle boots trimmed in fake fur. She was prepared for the bright Georgia sunshine with her rhinestone-studded sunglasses. She looked like Eartha Kitt as "Cat Woman." And like Eartha Kitt, Lena knew how to make a man's blood pressure rise. Her two brothers-in-law always felt nervous in her presence. Poor Joe Bamo became an absolute wreck having to drive her home to Oglethorpe from Macon. It was good that Nettie was with him. At least Elenora could focus on her sister for part of the ride.

When Lena was not sleeping on the long bus ride, she flirted with the driver from New York to Richmond, Virginia, then with the next driver to Atlanta, Georgia, and then with the last driver into Macon, Georgia. She made sure that she sat in the first seat opposite the driver's chair so that she could keep the man awake and amused. She told each driver about her career as an actress, singer and dancer. She told them about all of the men who had showered her with gifts. About all the men that she had given pleasure to over the years. She offered to pleasure her first driver if he could manage to control the bus and stay in his lane along I-95. As her nephew Marshall would say about his aunt Elenora, "She's just one ole hot mess!"

When Nettie and Joe Bamo spotted Elenora getting off the bus in Macon, they both hung their heads in shame.

Nettie nudged Joe Bamo, "Go on and help her with that suitcase."

He asked in his softest voice, "Do I have to?"

As he shuffled toward Elenora, she said to him, "Joe Bamo, get on over here and help me with this thing!"

He obeyed and stepped up his pace. He was always startled by the brashness and boldness of both Elenora and Rosalie. When he married into the Turner family, he felt overpowered by his sisters-in-law. Nettie stayed in the front seat of the car, waiting with her head still lowered. Joe Bamo put the suitcase in the backseat behind him; Elenora got in on the passenger side.

"Nettie, thanks for you and Joe Bamo coming to get me way up here in Macon," she said. "I declare, that was one hell of a bus ride," she added.

"No problem, Elenora," Nettie replied in an almost inaudible tone.

"The name is Lena, L-E-N-A, as in Lena Horne."

A smile crossed Nettie's face as they started what would be a long and uncomfortable ride back down to Oglethorpe.

Elenora talked all the way through Fort Valley, Marshallville and Montezuma. She talked all the way up to the front porch of Fannie Mae's house in Ogelthorpe, Georgia. She never tired of talking about her years away from Georgia — about the years that she spent on stage, and in piano bars and jazz cafés in New York City.

"I was the toast of Broadway, the toast of The Big Apple, the toast of the Great White Way!" she declared.

Actually of late, she had become fond of apple butter on toast. That's about all she could afford! Nettie, and Joe Bamo's ears were about to bleed from listening to Elenora's theatrical voice.

When Elenora walked through the front door with her leopard outfit, Rosalie said, "Oh hell no, no she didn't!"

That was followed by Marshall's declaration, "Miss Lena girl, you just too fine for words."

The two then traded air-kisses. Belle just shook her head and went back to what she was doing in the kitchen. Esau stared in wonderment and disbelief at his wife, son and sister-in-law. He thought to himself, "How did I ever get mixed up in this?"

Like Joe Bamo, Esau found himself uncomfortable around Elenora except for a different reason. He always felt that she was flirting with him. Sometimes she would corner him and press her body close to his. When he was dating Rosalie, he would knock at the front door of the Turner house and hope that she was dressed and ready to go. If she wasn't, Elenora tried to keep him entertained until her sister came into the living room. She would sit opposite him with her legs spread apart so he could see her underpants. By the time Rosalie was ready, Esau would be perspiring from nervousness. Elenora seemed to be amused by all of this. For her it was just a game. She liked to watch him squirm.

Christine and Horace Lee sat on the sofa looking like twins rather than lovers.

Christine merely sneered and rolled her eyes at her younger sister and mumbled to herself, "That bitch is crazier than when she left Georgia."

Horace Lee was too scared to even look in Elenora's direction for fear that Christine would snatch him by the collar. Joe Bamo placed Elenora's suitcase just inside the front door, and then he and Nettie beat a hasty retreat to their own quiet house across from the cemetery. They always used to say to one another, "Dead folks don't talk; they sure don't make noise; and they makes good neighbors."

There they were under Fannie Mae's roof: Belle, Rosalie, Christine, Elenora, Esau, Marshall and Horace Lee. The only two missing were Nettie and Joe Bamo. That didn't matter much because they were always so quiet that they would not have even been noticed in the presence of Rosalie, Elenora and Marshall. Nettie and Joe Bamo with their painful stillness would have made them almost invisible in the continuous noise kept up by the other three.

Belle walked out of her mother's kitchen and asked, "Elenora, do you want to freshen up from your long trip before you sit down for dinner?"

Elenora replied, "Yes, but please call me Lena, L-E-N-A, as in Lena Horne!"

Christine had about all that she could take of Elenora "Girlie" Lena Turner. "Don't you come up in here with all that Lena Horne, Dorothy Dandridge and Lana Turner bullshit!

Our mama's gone now, and the rest of us don't give a damn about that nonsense. I guess you going to think you is Halle Berry next?" she continued.

Elenora, with her hands on her hips revealing her shapely figure under her leopard swing coat, sashayed from side to side as she threw back her head and left the room.

Marshall snapped his fingers three times in a wide circle and said, "Miss Fannie Mae's girls, don't y'all act like this! Grandma and God are watching you."

"And, God don't like ugly," piped in Rosalie.

Esau tried to change the mood by saying, "You know now that Barack Obama is the new president, we all need to act more civilized toward one another."

Rosalie just looked in his direction and said, "You better put your joke book up!" and that was the end of his conversation.

Esau Tate knew his place, and his place was not in the middle of any conversation involving his wife, Rosalie, his son Marshall and another Turner sister.

Belle had prepared a spread just like Fannie Mae would have done if she were still living. She cooked baked hen and dressing, pole beans, creamed corn, cabbage, collard greens, pork chops, rice and gravy, homemade biscuits, and for dessert pecan pie and bread pudding.

When Rosalie saw the food on the table, she yelled out, "Ooh child, look what you get when you're lucky!"

The dinner reminded everyone of Fannie Mae and how much they would miss her. It was a bittersweet reunion for the Turner sisters. They had come together for the saddest of all occasions — to bury their beloved mother.

To try to fit in with the family, Horace Lee Miller volunteered to say grace before dinner. "Dear Lord, thank you for this gathering of Miss Fannie Mae's kinfolk. Heavenly Father, please bless them and keep them healthy, safe and free from harm. Bless her spirit, oh Lord, and bless this food that has been prepared in her memory. Bless this family. Amen."

Christine and Elenora looked at each other in a loving and sisterly way; they smiled and said, "Amen."

The two of them being the youngest were always the last to be fed at the Turner dinner table. After grace was said at a Turner dinner, their father, Henry, helped his plate, then Fannie Mae, and then the daughters, starting with Belle and ending with Elenora. If there was fried chicken for dinner, by the time it got to Christine and Elenora, there would only be two wings left; however, they always knew that Fannie Mae had held back a special surprise for them. The way that they looked at one another and smiled on this day was the same way that they knowingly looked at each other back then. Theirs was a bond that could not be broken no matter how long they had been apart. They were sisters who did not always get along, but sisters all the same.

Christine's cold reception toward Elenora when she arrived was rooted in jealousy and a need to protect her heart and her man. It was a defensive move on her part. She knew that given the opportunity these two would find a way to flirt with each other. Christine did not trust Horace Lee, and she trusted her baby sister even less. However, it would not take them long to recapture the friendship that they had shared as young girls.

After dinner, Rosalie, Christine and Elenora cleaned up the kitchen while Belle sat at the table like their mother used to do. It was just like old times when they were girls growing up in Henry and Fannie Mae Turner's house. They reminisced about those days and wished that Nettie and Joe Bamo had not left before dinner; however, they understood their need for peace and quiet.

Sometimes Rosalie could not even stand to be alone with her own self. She wondered how on earth poor Esau ever managed. When there were just the three of them in the Turner household, Belle, Nettie and Rosalie, it was easy for Nettie to find a place to hide away from Rosalic's ranting. Now she had her own house to hide in. It was not that she did not love her younger sisters, but Rosalie, Christine and Elenora under the same roof again was too much to bear.

They all sat around the parlor talking about how it was growing up in the strict household run by Henry and Fannie Mae. They talked about how boys were not allowed past the front porch. If they had to go to the bathroom, they would have to use the outhouse that Henry Turner used because he shared a house filled with a wife and five daughters. They talked about the three brothers who did not live beyond birth, Henry Jr., James and Thomas. It seemed that back then Fannie Mae always had a baby growing in her belly. Henry did not plan to stop until a boy child survived past birth. He finally gave up after the difficult birth of Elenora nearly took his wife from him.

They talked about how it would have been a lot easier on the five girls if the boys had survived. No chopping wood.

No hauling water from the well to the kitchen and for bathing. No plowing the fields, planting and harvesting. Things would certainly have been easier had the Ku Klux Klan not taken their grandpa Buck many years before and placed a curse upon the Turner family that prevented the boys from surviving. They talked about their crushes on boys they were never allowed to date. About how Henry Turner kept a watchful eye on the front porch from the parlor whenever a boy came courting.

Things were harder on Belle being the oldest child. The strictness eased a little with each of the other four girls. Henry and Fannie Mae never worried much about Nettie. She was so quiet and scared of folks that she never strayed far from her mama and daddy. Rosalie was the middle child who caused them to really worry. She was rebellious, but knew not to test Henry's lack of patience for foolishness. Christine always talked about running away from Oglethorpe, Georgia. She got no further than Atlanta.

Then there was Elenora who was the first to lose her virginity while living under her parents' roof. She gave herself completely to John Henry Johnson back up in the woods while they were still in high school. Other girls in Oglethorpe resisted his irresistible good looks and persistent advances. Elenora wanted John Henry as much if not more than he wanted her. They managed to continue to sneak around despite the fact that Henry Turner kept a close eye on them. Belle, Rosalie and Christine teased Elenora about seeing John Henry again. The last time she saw him was at her daddy's funeral back in 1992. They had a reunion of sorts back then for "old time's sake." They disregarded the rumors that they just might be half-siblings. John Henry was the only one from the Johnson family to attend Henry Turner's funeral, which started the gossip tongues wagging again.

Belle waited until everybody fell asleep or went to bed in Fannie Mae's house. She then slipped out and headed back to her own house through the clearing in the woods. Tomorrow was another day. They would all head over to Meadows Oglethorpe Funeral Chapel to preview Miss Fannie Mae's body before the wake that evening and the funeral at the church the following day.

Belle found it hard to fall asleep that night. She lay awake thinking that if she had spent the night with her mother on New Year's Eve, she might still be alive. Instead she attended Watch Night service at New Ebenezer First Missionary Baptist Church with her friend Adele Hammond. Before Fannie Mae became ill, it had been their annual tradition to attend service together on New Year's Eve. Now that her mother was gone, it would just be she and Adele. Nettie and Joe Bamo were in church that night as well, sitting in a corner by themselves. At the stroke of midnight that night, they could all hear from the church the sounds of revelers shooting guns off in the distance, and Belle thought of her mother sleeping alone in her bed. After the Watch Night service was over, Belle drove past her mother's house on her way home. If only she had stopped.

CHAPTER 7

A SLEEPING ANGEL (ISN'T SHE LOVELY?)

After breakfast the five Turner sisters, Joe Bamo, Esau and Marshall headed over to Meadows Oglethorpe Funeral Chapel to preview Fannie Mae's body before the wake and viewing that evening. Horace Lee Miller drove over to Ellaville to visit with his family and to see his old friends.

Christine warned him not to go looking up any of his old girlfriends. "Don't forget, I can tell if you've been with some ugly backwoods 'skank,'" she warned him.

When Horace Lee pulled into Samuel and Hortense Miller's front yard in Ellaville, he knew that they were at home. His daddy's old Chevrolet faced out toward the road with the front bumper held on with sticky glue-trap pest-control tape with symbols of a mouse, roach and an ant on it. He decided that he would tell his father to replace that tape with masking tape or duct tape to hold the bumper in place. Christine would have recommended using "masculine tape" or "duck tape."

Shortly after Horace Lee arrived at his parents' home, his old girlfriend Priscilla Jenkins stopped by. His sister Carrie Lee had called and told her that he was coming for a visit. Priscilla wore a rabbit-fur jacket with a red mini-skirt, black fishnet stockings and black-patent leather boots with four-inch heels. She was dressed to impress and seduce Horace Lee Miller. Her freshly tightened hair weave was long and flowing. She invited him to stop by her trailer on his way back to Oglethorpe. While he felt tempted, he believed that Christine did have a tremendous sense of smell. So instead of taking Priscilla up on her offer, he wisely decided to stay put and enjoy the visit with his mother, father, sister and brother. He did not want to take the chance of Christine smelling "skank" on him. Horace Lee had not regained her trust ever since she knocked that woman off the barstool at Bigelow's Bar and Grill.

Belle and Meadows Oglethorpe Funeral Chapel had followed Fannie Mae's wishes down to every small detail, just as she had wanted. Her casket had a pearlescent finish in the color of Robin's egg blue, lined with fluffy white satin. As Belle instructed, the morticians did her makeup minimally. They lightly powdered her face, with just a hint of color on her cheeks and lips, and they had trimmed her hair in a short and rather plain hairstyle. Fannie Mae's pearl necklace, bracelet and earrings added just the right touch. She was dressed in a heavenly blue-silk shaded gown, tied with a white sash neatly in a bow about the waist, which hung neatly down the front. The bow was nothing of the magnitude that Marshall would have tied on his grandmother's body. When Marshall offered his assistance in dressing Fannie Mae for her funeral, Belle turned a deaf ear.

She was an angel in death as she was in life. She was the mother who gave so much and asked for so little in return. The mortuary made sure she had the proper funeral and burial that she always dreamed of. Strict instructions forbade any fuss made over her casket at her funeral service. The funeral director ordered the family to conduct themselves with dignity and respect — that was all that Fannie Mae had asked of them. If any of her daughters or her only grandchild wanted to whoop and holler, they had better get it out of their systems now during the preview of her body. "Me and God will be watchin'!" she warned.

To avoid a cluster of emotions all at once in previewing the body of Fannie Mae Turner, Pastor Hicks and his wife, Ethel, had both suggested that the sisters view her body separately and in the same order in which they were born unto it. Belle would be first, then Nettie and Joe Bamo, then Rosalie, Esau and Marshall, then Christine, and finally, Elenora.

Belle — who had spent the most time with her mother in her later years, who had cared for her right up until her death, and who had cooked and cleaned for her — spent the shortest amount of time previewing Fannie Mae's body. As far as her mother was concerned, Belle had earned her angel wings. Belle felt comfort in knowing that she was able to answer the call, to be there when needed. If she had married or moved away from Oglethorpe, things might have been different.

"Goodbye, dear Mother, I'll see you in heaven," Belle said as she bent over to kiss her mother's forehead.

Next Nettie and Joe Bamo entered the chapel, walking quietly and slowly as always. As they approached the casket, Joe Bamo put an arm around his wife's shoulder and held her steady.

Nettie's eyes moistened with silent tears to match her nearly silent voice, "Goodbye, Mama, I love you."

"Goodbye, Mrs. Turner," uttered Joe Bamo almost as silently as his wife.

They both promised to keep an eye on her grave not only from across the road, but to make sure that her resting place would be kept neat and clean.

When it was Rosalie, Esau and Marshall's turn to enter, Esau stood erect, wrapped an arm around his wife and son and ushered them toward Fannie Mae's casket. He held steady and allowed them each to grieve in their own way. Esau never let go of Rosalie and Marshall. Rosalie started speaking in tongue, a side of his wife that he had never seen before.

Marshall danced, twirled and shouted, "Mama girl! Mama girl! Mama girl!"

Somehow, Esau found the strength to hold them both until they crumpled into his arms. He ushered them out of the chapel as steady as he had walked them in. His duty was to be there for his wife and son. Rosalie, for the first time in a long while, felt safe and secure in her husband's care.

Christine leaned close to her mother's body in the casket, "Mama, please forgive me for leaving you. I never meant to leave you, but I had to go. Please understand that I always loved you, and I always will."

She clasped her hands over Fannie Mae's hands and kissed her gently. Christine promised her mother that she and Horace Lee would eventually get married and stop living in sin. She told her mother that if she ever had a daughter, she would name her Fannie Mae Miller.

Elenora strode into the chapel wearing her sunglasses to hide her already-reddened eyes. She had cried throughout the night. She wished that she had returned to Oglethorpe more often over the years. Only her mother knew why she left in the first place. She was pregnant with John Henry Johnson's child. Her mother's intuition told her that the child Elenora was carrying was no doubt the product of half-siblings. Fannie Mae had sent her off with her blessings. Even though Fannie Mae prayed daily for all of her daughters, she prayed extra hard for Elenora.

She had been sent up north to New York to Fannie Mae's cousin Martha to have an abortion. Because of her inner shame, she never returned until her father's death in 1992 and now again in 2009 because of her mother's death.

Elenora took her sunglasses off as she approached the casket and simply said, "Mama, thank you!"

She turned on her heels, returned her sunglasses to her face, and walked away, feeling that she had accomplished the greatest performance of her life. She was now at peace with and proud to be Elenora "Girlie" Turner, daughter of Henry and Fannie Mae Turner of Oglethorpe, Georgia. There would no longer be a Lena Turner. She would no longer have flights of fantasy about Lana Turner and Lena Horne. From now on, she would be just plain, old Elenora.

That evening, many friends, neighbors and distant relatives stopped by Meadows Oglethorpe Funeral Chapel to visit with and to comfort Fannie Mae's girls. They came to sit in wake of one of Oglethorpe's most beloved citizens. They came to pay tribute to Fannie Mae Turner, and acknowledge her life and her presence in theirs. They came from all over Macon County, from Oglethorpe, Montezuma, Ideal and Marshallville (for which her only grandchild was named). They came from Ellaville, Buena Vista, and all the way from Albany and Americus. They sang her praises. Many commented that despite her fragility, "God gave her the strength to make it to the polls to cast her vote for Barack Obama. She was part of history. She helped to elect the first black president of the United States of America."

They talked about the pies and cakes that she would bake for their families during times of bereavement, even when she wasn't able to bake for her own. They talked about her service to her church community and her dedication to her faith. "She was a soldier in God's army," many of them said.

Her wake attracted people of all races: whites, blacks, Koreans and Mexicans. There were people from all walks of life: the wealthy, poor and middle class. There were politicians, law enforcement officers, educators, factory workers, merchants, government officials, and military personnel. Even two of Marshall's drag queen friends, Neesha and Wendy, drove up from Albany. They arrived in full drag, makeup, hair extensions, eyelashes and fur coats. Real fur, not fake fur like Elenora had arrived in. As one might imagine, they were certainly not politically correct. As a matter of fact, they were way over the top! Belle was certain that Fannie Mae's spirit hovered somewhere above this gathering, feeling proud, amused, and praying for them all.

The guest book for visitors to sign had every page filled, which was a true testament to how much everyone loved Fannie Mae Turner. When word spread that she had died, the entire community of Oglethorpe and Macon County went into shock and sadness to hear of her passing. Fannie Mae Turner was the matriarch of one of the most upstanding families in Oglethorpe. She earned a well-known reputation for being a model citizen and a dedicated member of the community in every corner of Macon County from Ideal to Montezuma. She was the daughter of Buck and Jesse Jessup, founding members of New Ebenezer First Missionary Baptist Church; and she and her husband, Henry, had raised their five daughters in the same church. Fannie Mae Turner was as solid as they came in this part of South Georgia.

CHAPTER 8

I'M COMING HOME (SEE YOU IN HEAVEN)

The mourners gathered at New Ebenezer First Missionary Baptist Church for the home-going services for Fannie Mae Turner. The sanctuary was adorned with flower arrangements and sprays in every shade and variety of blue flower that one could imagine along with white roses, lilies and orchids. Two large urns filled with long-stemmed, blue-and-white flowers sat on either side of the pulpit. The choir members stood in the choir stand, they wore white robes with light-blue bibs and tassels. The deaconesses, usherettes and Women's Auxiliary members were all dressed in white. The church nurses wore crisp-white uniforms and caps. The deacons and the ushers wore dark-blue suits, white shirts and light-blue neckties. Pastor Hicks wore his light-blue suit and Ethel Hicks wore her powder-blue coatdress with matching hat, shoes and gloves, just as Fannie Mae had requested. White covers embossed with blue crosses sheathed the backs of the heavy-wooden pulpit chairs. A white-satin runner with blue fringes and tassels draped over the lectern from which Pastor Hicks would speak.

The immediate family arrived in a Meadows Oglethorpe Funeral Chapel white-stretch limousine that stopped just behind the white hearse already parked in front of the church. Fannie Mae's five daughters and her grandson, Marshall, sat in the limo. Esau Tate, Joe Bamo, Horace Lee Miller and Adele Hammond arrived in the second car, while the cars of other family members and close friends followed in procession.

As the cars pulled in, it happened to be an unseasonably warm, bright and sunny day for January. The heavenly blue sky above was so vivid with huge, fluffy white clouds. It presented the perfect day for a funeral — that is, if there is such a thing. The perfect weather befitting a nearly perfect lady who truly was a child of God. It has always been said, "Any day above ground is a good day." Or, "The weather is always warmer above ground."

Pastor Hicks led the family into the church while reciting the 23rd Psalm. Belle and Adele Hammond walked in just behind Pastor Hicks, followed by Nettie and Joe Bamo, then Rosalie and Esau, Christine and Horace Lee, and Marshall escorted his aunt Elenora. All of Fannie Mae's girls were dressed in beautiful white as she had requested. Belle and Nettie wore sensible-yet-stylish white dresses. Rosalie wore a frilly white Chiffon two-piece dress with ruffles around the neck and a big white bow in her hair, as was her style. Christine dressed in a white polyester pantsuit and white pumps from Payless. And,

Elenora gave the flock of mourners just what they came to see. When she walked in escorted by Marshall, she wore a 1960s vintage winter-white Chanel suit with a white camellia flower on the lapel, a white wool cloche style hat with white leather hatband and bow, white kidskin leather three-quarter length gloves, white leather high heels and a clutch bag. She accessorized with a simple single strand of pearls, and her signature sunglasses with white mother of pearl frames. Elenora "Girlie" Turner looked like a movie star. Many of those gathered had not seen her since 1992. Many just came to gawk at the legendary daughter of Henry and Fannie Mae Turner of Macon County, Georgia, even if she was just a legend in her own mind.

While Marshall chose to wear white like his mother and his aunts, he surprised everyone with a light-blue necktie rather than his signature flowing neck scarf. This act paid tribute to how much he loved and respected his grandmother. It was also a tribute to how much he wanted to please his parents, Esau and Rosalie Tate. The onlookers had expected Marshall to be his usual flamboyantly gay self. He fooled them all. He was actually happy that he was not the center of attention or the subject of small-town gossip. Marshall Tate had his share of scandals that stretched from Albany to Oglethorpe and back. He gladly deferred that distinction to his aunt Elenora — and, she was happy to accept the honor.

Members of Meadows Oglethorpe Funeral Chapel staff stood by Fannie Mae's casket for the final glance and moments of silent love and reflection by the family, who were then seated in the pews reserved for them. After the family was seated, the choir sang one of Fannie's Mae's favorite songs "Lord Don't Move That Mountain," led by Anita Robinson, bringing tears, multiple "amens," hand waving, and a rising of emotions. Ms. Robinson and the choir followed immediately with "Long As I Got King Jesus (Don't Need Nobody Else)." This song offered the perfect lead-in for Pastor Hicks and his ministerial staff. He read Fannie Mae's favorite scriptures, which were followed by Ethel Hicks's beautiful and eloquent reading of her 'Life Story,' acknowledgements and resolutions.

Next there was a surprise solo selection. As the musicians started the intro to "Amazing Grace," a voice rose up from the pews: "Amazing Grace, how sweet the sound, that saved a wretch like me. I once was lost, but now am found, was blind, but now I see." The surprise gesture came from Elenora Turner as she walked up to the front of the church, singing the phrase. She placed her right hand on her mother's closed casket and sang like an angel. Anita Robinson offered Elenora her microphone, which she refused. Her voice rang out with vocal clarity and intense feeling all through the sanctuary. Elenora was a vision in white — a vision of what heaven must be like and an angel to welcome her mother into the Pearly Gates. Her voice brought the gatherers to their feet, with hands waving in the air, and swaying from side to side. They were still standing when she returned singing to take her seat. Handkerchiefs wiped away tears and were used to also wave through the air. Elenora's rendition was the second greatest performance of her life. She did what she always wanted to do, sing to her mother, "Her Amazing Grace who saved a wretch like her."

Pastor Hicks' eulogy of Fannie Mae Turner turned out just as she requested, short, sweet, and to the point. She did not want prolonged preaching over her body. She had attended too many funerals throughout her 86 years that were so long and drawn out, that even the families wished that they would end.

Pastor Hicks praised her dedication to the Lord, her family, her friends, her neighbors, and to the community-at-large.

He said, "Fannie Mae Turner was a shining example for all of us to live by. She served the Lord and loved her family unconditionally. Belle, Nettie, Rosalie, Christine and Elenora, your mother loved each of you equally. She loved each of you for your individuality and uniqueness. Marshall, she was proud to have you as a grandson. She smiled with joy each time she spoke of each of you. Joe Bamo and Esau, she was so happy when you married into the Turner family. In closing, I am proud to say that Fannie Mae Turner loved us all, and we were truly blessed by her presence in our lives. May she rest in peace for all eternity."

After the eulogy, there was another solo selection by Anita Robinson, the benediction, and then a closing hymn by the choir, "Soon and Very Soon." Pastor Hicks led the recessional from the sanctuary followed by the family, the flower attendants, and the pallbearers with Fannie Mae Turner's casket.

En route to the Oglethorpe Cemetery, the funeral cortege made a pass by the home place of Fannie Mae Turner. They passed the land where her father, Buck, was born. They passed the land where Fannie Mae was born. They passed by where she and Henry Turner raised their five daughters and where she died. The long line of cars proceeded through the center of town past City Hall on Chatham Street. Fannie Mae Turner so loved the city of Oglethorpe on the west bank of the Flint River that she never left the place she called home. She was finally saying, "Goodbye."

There were so many cars in the funeral procession at the cemetery that they extended all the way out to the road. The mourners gathered around the open gravesite that sat under a white canopy. Light-blue velvet covers sheathed the chairs designated for the family. Pallbearers escorted family members to their seats. Before sitting down, Nettie and Joe Bamo paused momentarily to stare at their home across the road from the cemetery. They were getting a new neighbor, her beloved mother, Fannie Mae. Being in the cemetery for the first time since Henry Turner died in 1992 felt surreal for Nettie and Joe Bamo. Heretofore, they only watched from their front porch or upstairs window.

After Pastor Hicks committed her body to the earth, the pallbearers, friends and relatives placed white-and-blue flowers upon her coffin. Her immediate family members placed white lilies in the sign of the cross: Belle, then Nettie and Joe Bamo, followed by Rosalie, Esau and Marshall, Christine and finally Elenora.

The entire gathering looked skyward as Pastor Hicks recited Psalm 55:6, "Oh that I had wings like a dove, for then I would fly away and be at rest." A participant released a flock of white doves from a basket. They soared toward the heavens carrying Fannie Mae's spirit upon their wings.

Fannie Mae would have been so proud of the dignity and grace with which her family had conducted their behavior during her home-going services and interment. She would have been especially proud to know that her baby girl, Elenora, had finally found her voice.

Back at the church hall, the members of the Women's Auxiliary had prepared a sumptuous feast in honor of their dearly departed sister in Christ, Fannie Mae Turner. The Turner sisters received their guests for fellowship in the manner in which their mother had taught them. Instead of being served by the Women's Auxiliary, the five sisters, Joe Bamo, Esau, Marshall and Horace Lee served the meal to family, friends and neighbors of Fannie Mae. The sisters donned aprons to protect their white funeral clothes and served plates that were dished up by their men folk. They were Fannie Mae's girls all over again, smiling, laughing, singing and dancing all around the church hall. Even the normally quiet Nettie took on a tone that was light, airy and gay.

Christine, Elenora and Marshall launched into a rendition of "Someday, We'll be Together." Marshall sang the Diana Ross lead with his aunts singing backup. "Fat Ethel" Hicks kicked off her powder-blue pumps and grabbed Pastor Hicks for a spotlight dance around the floor. She giggled like Gloria the hippo would if she were dancing with Melman the giraffe in "Madagascar 2." The entire church hall erupted into applause and laughter at the impromptu and unexpected entertainment. This was a happy repast celebration in honor of their beloved Fannie Mae Turner. The family and their guests lingered around longer than was customary for a repast held in the church hall. There was so much to say about Fannie Mae Turner, and no one was in a hurry to rush things along. The Women's Auxiliary served them tea, coffee, cakes and pies as the tribute continued.

CHAPTER 9

SHE LEAVES TO MOURN (PASS THE MOLASSES PLEASE)

The family of Fannie Mae Turner gathered around the breakfast table the day after her funeral. Belle had prepared a southern breakfast very much like her mother used to do for her husband and their five daughters. The table was laden with country ham, grits, red-eye gravy, slab bacon, country-style sausage patties, eggs scrambled with cheese, home-fried potatoes, homemade biscuits, blackberry jam and blackstrap molasses. When Esau Tate offered to say grace, his wife, Rosalie, and his son, Marshall, both beamed with pride.

"Dear God, bless this family, bless the spirit of Miss Fannie Mae, bless this food that thou and Belle hath put before us, bless us all, oh Lord, keep this family together forever, amen."

The others said, "Amen" in unison.

The food tasted as if Fannie Mae had reached from beyond

the grave and prepared it with her own hands. This was southern-style eating at its best. Christine and Elenora had missed out on the staples of home when they moved away to Atlanta and New York. Occasionally, Fannie Mae would have Belle send them both some homemade goodies from her kitchen back home in Oglethorpe, Georgia. Elenora was particularly fond of her mother's maple sugar pecan pie, and Christine's favorite gift from home was Fannie Mae's cured country ham slices. She used them sparingly until she received the next package from Belle. While country ham was readily available in Atlanta stores, there was something special about the way her mama made it. Horace Lee knew that he had been on his best behavior when Christine served him a thick slice of her precious country ham from home.

At the breakfast table that morning, they talked about Fannie Mae's funeral from the day before. They all congratulated Elenora on her surprise solo of "Amazing Grace."

Christine said to her baby sister, "Girl, you sure blew the doors off New Ebenezer First Missionary Baptist Church!"

Marshall chimed in, "Anita Robinson, you better move over Miss Thang, Elenora 'Girlie' Turner is back in town!" That statement was followed by his sound effects of hot bacon sizzling in a frying pan.

They all cracked up the way that Fannie Mae used to do after every visit from her only grandchild, Marshall Tate. He was a "mini-me" of his mother, Rosalie. Marshall spent so much time at the hem of her skirt. He was always interested in what his mother was doing or saying and never paid much attention to his father, Esau. At an early age, he began to mimic her mannerisms, words and actions, which clearly indicated that he was never going to be the boy that Esau Tate had hoped for.

At the age of two, he walked around the house and repeated, "Look what you get when you lucky," and, "You better put your joke book up."

He was the closest thing to the little girl that Rosalie had always wanted.

After congratulating Elenora on her vocal talents, the gossiping time was on! They found amusement in just about every little thing that they could remember from Fannie Mae's funeral.

"Ooh child, did you see the lace that Edna Green took from her half-slip and sewed up under her hat for a veil?" hollered Rosalie.

"And, that green suit and hat that Purvis Johnson had on, he looked just like the leprechaun straight off the Lucky Charms cereal box," offered Joe Bamo unexpectedly..

"How about those Edge sisters chewing Red Bull tobacco and spitting into Dixie cups?" asked Esau.

"What about Dottie Fields? Did you see that bleached-blonde nappy hair looking like an Afro-Brillo Pad? Ooh child, her eyebrows were painted on her forehead like Miss Joan Crawford!" Rosalie screamed. "And, what about that Carol Neptune walking up in the church with that man young enough to be her grandson, sat right down in front too? That woman's got no shame. Go on with your bad self, Miss Carol Neptune!" Rosalie was on a roll.

"OK, that's enough, Fannie Mae Turner would not approve of such talk," offered Nettie. And, the gossiping came to a screeching-ass halt. It ended abruptly because Nettie only spoke when she had something important to say. She always believed, "If you ain't got nothing good to say about somebody, you best keep quiet."

That was perfect timing for that kind of talk to end. Pastor Hicks, Ethel Hicks and Fannie Mae's attorney, Thomas Allen knocked at the front door.

Belle answered the door. "Good morning, Pastor Hicks, Mrs. Hicks, Mr. Allen. We were just finishing breakfast, want some?" she asked.

"No, thank you," said the three in one voice.

"We are here to discuss Fannie Mae's last wishes for her family," said attorney Thomas Allen. "My secretary, Helen Mills, helped Miss Fannie Mae prepare a message for all of you. Can we get everyone together here in the living room?" he requested.

Belle called her sisters, brothers-in-law, nephew and Horace Lee Miller to come in from the kitchen. Once they were all gathered and seated, Mr. Allen began to read the letter that Fannie Mae had written with the help of Helen Mills.

"Dear Fannie Mae's Girls,

I want each of you to know how much you were loved by me and your daddy, Henry. We loved each of you differently because each of you was so different. Belle, you were our first daughter and you reminded me so much of my daddy, we called you 'Lil Buck.' You have been with me the longest. Thank you for staying so close. You gave up your life to stay close to your mama. Nettie, you were so quiet, just like a doll baby, you were a little sister for Belle, so we called you 'Sis.' I was so glad that you found a good, quiet man like Joe Bamo to marry. Thanks for all the good fish that you and Joe Bamo gave me to cook and for us to eat. Rosalie, when you come along you looked just like me — long and the color of Georgia red clay — so we called you 'Big Red.' Thank you and Esau for giving me my one and only grandchild. Christine, you were so sweet just like molasses, we could just eat you up, so we called you 'Sweetie Pie.' I wish I could have made it up to Atlanta to visit you, but your telephone calls were just as good! Elenora, you were our last child, our baby girl, so your daddy called you 'Girlie.' And, you were to me better than any ole Lana Turner or Lena Horne. You were always my little actress. You were always singing and dancing in front of the mirror. I hope that you were able to sing at my funeral. I know that if you did, it was mighty good, child! Joe Bamo, Esau and Horace Lee, God gave us the three of you to replace the three sons that he saw fit to take away. Horace Lee, even though you didn't marry my 'Sweetie Pie' before I died, I hope that someday you will! Marshall, all I can say is that you are a funny boy. You made your grandma so happy. You made me laugh and smile even when I thought I couldn't. Boy, you is so funny, you could be on television. You were my child too, my special child. Mama Girl loved you just like God made you!

If Mr. Allen is reading you this letter that me and Ms. Mills done wrote, that means that I done gone home to be with the Lord. Sometimes, we have to lose the ones we love to know how much we love them. I sure knew that y'all loved me like I loved y'all. Mr. Thomas Allen has a box that I gave him to give to Pastor Hicks for y'all. Bye now. See y'all when y'all get to heaven. Praise God! Mama Fannie Mae."

Pastor Hicks produced a wooden box that had been hand-carved by Fannie Mae's daddy, Buck. The box had always been kept in the top of the closet in Fannie Mae's bedroom. No one ever dared look in this box because she always said, "That's personal and none of your business!" Now, their curiosity would be satisfied. Finally! Inside of the box were six envelopes addressed to Belle Turner, Nettie Bamo, Rosalie Tate, Christine Turner, Elenora "Lena" Turner and Marshall Tate. They were stacked in that same order in the box, from the first-born daughter to the last, then her grandson.

Attorney Thomas Allen told them, "If you want to share what is in each of your envelopes with the others, it would be OK by Fannie Mae's wishes."

It was decided by consensus that they would wait until dinner later that evening when there was only family present. They placed the wooden box on the mantelpiece in the living room.

Pastor Hicks, Mrs. Hicks and Mr. Allen left the Turner house; before leaving, Pastor Hicks said to them all, "Don't you all be strangers at New Ebenezer First Missionary Baptist Church now that Miss Fannie Mae is gone!"

He knew all too well that sometimes after the head of a family dies, their children stop coming to church. This would not be the case for Belle, Nettie and Joe Bamo. His comment was directed mostly to Rosalie, Esau, Marshall, Christine, Horace Lee and Elenora. He wanted them to feel welcome at New Ebenezer First Missionary Baptist Church whenever they were in Oglethorpe.

After the three visitors left, they all placed their envelopes back in the wooden box in the same order in which they had been taken out. The curiosity was eating away at them, but they had all agreed to wait until dinnertime. Marshall and Rosalie were reminded not to peek while no one else was looking. They were the only two who could not be trusted to honor the agreement. Each time one of them passed the box on the mantel, there was an urge to look inside, but there were too many pairs of watchful eyes around. They would just have to wait until later.

CHAPTER 10

WE ARE FAMILY (I GOT ALL MY SISTERS AND ME)

After Pastor Hicks, Mrs. Hicks and Thomas Allen left Fannie Mae's house, the Turner sisters cleared away the breakfast dishes and cleaned the kitchen spotless. It was just like when they were girls growing up under their parents' roof. The rest of the day, they spent reminiscing about their parents, Fannie Mae and Henry. They talked about how strict Henry Turner was, and how he used to watch every boy who came around, with a close, scrutinizing eye that would put the fear in the boys' hearts. They talked about Elenora sneaking around behind her father's back with John Henry Johnson. Christine used to play lookout for her younger sister. They had a set of signals to alert when the coast was clear or when there was danger nearby. Christine would cough either once or twice accordingly. When hearing her coughs, Henry Turner demanded that Christine take the nastiest remedies he could find. Sometimes she had to take one for the team by swallowing a dose of castor oil, cod liver oil or Three Sixes (666) cold medicine. He was probably wise to Christine covering for Elenora and John Henry; he derived great pleasure in seeing her face contort and twist in anguish.

Their parents chided Belle for beating up on boys who tried to get too close to her younger sisters. She was older and stronger than the boys who came around. Since they could not match Belle, they just gave up trying. Nettie was teased by her sisters for finding a man quieter than she was — and for always smelling like worms and fish since she fondly loved to go fishing and mess around in the water."

"You and Joe Bamo are a match made in heaven," said Elenora. It was the first time that Elenora had ever commended Nettie for her choice of a husband. Usually, she did nothing but ridicule.

As for Christine, they gave her grief for meeting a man all the way up in Atlanta — one whom she could have met just one county over in Ellaville. They also gave her a good teasing for meeting a man with three gold teeth to match her own.

Then they gave Rosalie a hard time for being so domineering over Esau and Marshall and for monopolizing every conversation.

"You are not what you get when you're lucky! Now, you put your joke book up!" Christine told Rosalie.

Uncharacteristically, Rosalie just shrugged her shoulders in silence. She had absolutely nothing to say that would counter the truth.

They talked about their favorite schoolteachers, and the fun times that they used to have in their various classes, clubs and activities. Belle's favorite classes included sewing and home economics, but she also excelled at sports. Nettie joined the 4-H Club, which prepared her for her love of nature and the outdoors. Rosalie was on the debate team and handily used her skills. She could out talk and argue the best of opponents. She always had the last word whether right or wrong. Christine took arts and crafts classes, and, of course, Elenora was into drama and dance. That was the beginning of her interest in all things Hollywood and Broadway. She studied the acting nuances of Bette Davis, Vivien Leigh, Olivia de Havilland, Susan Hayward and Loretta Young as well as her idols, black actresses Lena Horne and Dorothy Dandridge. These women of stage and screen helped to shape her fantasies of fortune and fame.

While the ladies reflected on their childhood and growth into young women, Joe Bamo, Esau, Marshall and Horace Lee rearranged the furniture in the dining room, living room and three bedrooms. They swept the floors and took all of the area rugs outside to air out. Then they brought boxes down from the attic for the Turner sisters to go through. The sisters needed to decide what to give away to Goodwill or the Salvation Army and what to keep for themselves.

While in the attic, the men found a wealth of history of the Turner and Jessup families. Trunks and boxes were filled with old, loose photographs, photo albums, and family bibles with the birth dates of the ancestors listed dating back to the pre-Civil War period. They found a box that contained Fannie Mae's mother's wedding dress, high-button shoes and lace gloves. A page from a ledger listed the names of freed slaves who had once been the property of one Thomas Archibald Meade of Montezuma, Georgia.

Later that afternoon, some of the members of the Women's Auxiliary from Fannie Mae's church dropped off food to the Turner household for supper. They brought a Honey-Baked ham, fried chicken, macaroni and cheese, green-bean casserole, collard greens, corn muffins and apple cobbler. All Belle had to make to go with dinner was sweet iced tea. It was customary for the Women's Auxiliary of New Ebenezer First Missionary Baptist Church to bring a hot supper to the bereaved family on the next day after a funeral took place. It took the pressure off and allowed the family to adjust to their loss without having to worry about making dinner. There were always extra mouths to feed, and there was plenty of food to go around.

After a hard day of organizing and cleaning Fannie Mae's house, the whole family sat down in the dining room for dinner at about 6:00 p.m. In the center of the table sat the wooden box that Pastor Hicks had delivered earlier. It was the same beautiful hand-carved box that Fannie Mae had always kept hidden in the top of her closet. After Esau said grace, they filled their plates with the delicious food that had been prepared for them. Everyone stared at the box with much interest and curiosity throughout dinner.

Finally, Marshall asked, "Are we going to just sit here and stare at that damn box?"

He then stood up, took the box, and set it in front of

his aunt Belle. She opened the box and took out the envelope addressed to her, and then it was passed on to Nettie, then to Rosalie, Christine, Elenora, and back to Marshall. Once they each had their respective envelopes in hand, Belle opened hers first. Inside it contained a check for $20,000 and a note written in Fannie Mae's own handwriting on her very own stationery.

"Dear Lil Buck,

I know that you will look after your sisters when I am gone. Thank you for all that you have done for me. Please take the quilt from my bed that my mama and I made. It will keep you warm at night.

Love,

Mama."

Next came Nettie's turn. It also contained a check for the same amount and a note that read:

"Dear Sis,

Buy you and Joe Bamo some new fishing poles and lots of worms; keep an eye on my grave from across that road.

Love,

Mama."

"Dear Big Red,

You and Esau take that cruise that you been talking so much about, have a good time for your mama too!

Love y'all."

"Dear Sweetie Pie,

You and Horace Lee think about getting married soon you hear and don't go spending all this money on no fool wedding. Your mama, daddy and God will be watching you now."

Inside Elenora's envelope was yet another check for $20,000, the deed to Fannie Mae's property and a note that read:

"Girlie,

It's about time you come on back home to Oglethorpe where you belong. The Lord won't mind sure enough.

Love,

Mama."

The rest of the family looked at Elenora as she read her note aloud. She looked up toward heaven and simply said with tears in her eyes, "Yes, Mama, I'm coming home."

Her sisters all beamed with joy at hearing her decision to return home for good. Marshall was the last to open his envelope. He was so nervous that his hands trembled and sweat beaded up on his forehead. He had a check for $10,000 and a note that read:

"Marshall Honey,

This ought to buy you plenty of them silk scarves you love so much and plenty of shoes to match.

Love you always,

Mama Girl."

There was laughter in between the tears. Even Joe Bamo, Esau and Horace Lee had moist eyes.

Fannie Mae Turner had sold off part of the land that her own mother, Jesse, had left to her. The money had been placed in a savings account, earning enough interest over the years for her to leave her daughters $20,000 each and her grandson $10,000. How she kept this money a secret for so many years was beyond anyone's imagination. Especially, since she had five daughters living in the house. Her personal banker, Daniel Ware, helped to keep this information confidential and provided Fannie Mae with an annual statement of her account. Fannie Mae had given Pastor Hicks the power of attorney to withdraw the money from her account and issue the checks for her beneficiaries. Fannie Mae's girls, Joe Bamo, Esau, Horace Lee and Marshall all held hands around the table and said, "Thank you, Jesus!"

Each of the Turner daughters would mourn Fannie Mae in their own special way. They would each mourn her passing in accordance with their individual personalities. Belle would probably get up every morning and look through her curtains at Fannie Mae's house through the clearing, wanting her mother to be there waiting for her daily visit. Fixing breakfast and dinner for just herself would be a lonely ordeal. On Sundays, she would likely slide into the same pew where she and Fannie Mae sat with Nettie and Joe Bamo and feel the emptiness. Nettie and Joe Bamo would mostly feel the affect on Sundays and each time that they left their home directly across from the cemetery. Rosalie, Esau and Marshall would still drive up to Oglethorpe every third Sunday, but Fannie Mae would not be there. Christine would probably return to Atlanta and make sure that she became Mrs. Horace Lee Miller in honor of her mother's wishes. Elenora had already promised to return home to Fannie Mae's house and recapture the life that she left behind so many years before. All of the sisters pledged to remain close and to practice sisterly love the way that they were taught by their beloved mother, Fannie Mae. They were indeed "Miss Fannie Mae's Girls," and that would always be true.

CHAPTER 11

WILL YOU MARRY ME? (WELCOME TO THE FAMILY)

Horace Lee Miller decided not to wait until they got back to Atlanta to ask Christine Turner to be his wife. On the third day after Fannie Mae's funeral, he popped the question to his long time girlfriend. That evening he asked Christine to take a drive with him over to Ellaville to visit his parents to have dinner. Even though she wanted to spend as much time as possible with her sisters before heading back to Atlanta, she reluctantly agreed to go with him.

When they arrived at the Miller's home, Horace Lee's mother, father, sister and brother were waiting and dinner was on the table. Christine had met his family on a number of occasions at their home in Ellaville and during the visits they made to Atlanta to see Horace Lee and other relatives. They were a very close-knit, good Southern Baptist family. The Millers were always involved in their children's activities from elementary school through college. Their son Bobby Lee Miller had attended Clark Atlanta University. They became very familiar with the city while visiting him. The Millers also loved to visit churches in the Atlanta area. After attending church, they would sometimes meet Horace Lee and Christine at The Green Manor Restaurant in Union City, Georgia for Sunday brunch. The Green Manor serves one of the best southern-style brunch buffets in Georgia, with a wide assortment of food items. They offer fried chicken, ham, baked chicken, fish, turkey and dressing, corn, field peas, collard and turnip greens, cornbread, rolls, salad, etc. For dessert, they have banana pudding, cakes, pies and sweet-potato soufflé. Their signature beverage, a combination of peach punch and sweet iced tea, was part of a veritable feast for the soul after the spirit has been renewed.

The patrons of The Green Manor, mostly churchgoers, are as varied as the menu selections. The whites normally arrive between 11:30 a.m. and 12:30 p.m., because their church services are short in comparison to black churches. The black patrons usually arrive between 1:00 p.m. and 2:00 p.m. because of the lateness of their worship services. It is interesting to also note the difference in the dress attire of the two groups. Whites normally dress in muted colors of gray, tan, blue, black or brown. On the other hand, blacks dress very colorfully. The black women wear very decorative hats and clothing in every shade and color of the rainbow. The black men are often adorned in suits of the brightest colors, mustard yellow, peacock blue, lavender, purple, lime green, ruby red or rust. Oftentimes their shoes and hats match the color of their suits, and their suit jackets range in length from hip to mid-calf. While there is a big cultural divide in the choice of attire between these two groups, there is not in their dining habits as evidenced by The Green Manor, which is a melting pot of southern cultures, southern comforts and southern culinary delights.

Christine always enjoyed dining with the Millers. It gave her an opportunity to get to know the parents of Horace Lee Miller, the man who she loved so much. The dinner that included his sister and brother made her feel even more a part of his family. It meant a lot to Christine since she had just lost her own mother and was just becoming closer to her sisters who she had missed so much quality time with. She now had a sense of purpose and belonging, not only to the Turners but also to the Millers.

After dinner, Christine, Horace Lee, his parents and siblings retired to the living room. She felt so comfortable seeing how close Horace Lee was to his family. As the eldest of the Miller children, his younger brother and sister looked up to him. Christine was beginning to feel that his family had the same wish that Fannie Mae had before she died — that she and Horace Lee would one day marry.

Later in the evening, Horace Lee asked if he could just say a prayer before he and Christine left: "Dear God, please bless my family who has stood by me in good times and bad. Bless them and keep them in your care. Heavenly Father, I thank you also for making it possible for me to find Christine, the woman who makes me so happy every day of my life. Dear God, I ask that you bless me with the gift of her love forever in my life. Dear God, I ask that she agrees to be my wife."

He turned and looked at Christine with ring in hand and said, "Before God and my family, Christine Turner will you marry me?"

Christine with tears in her eyes said, "Yes, of course, I will marry you Horace Lee Miller!"

He placed the engagement ring upon her finger and kissed her gently. Before they left his parents home, his father pulled out a jug of homemade wine to toast the couple. The Millers all hugged their future daughter and sister-in-law. Christine was so happy, she could not wait to get back to Fannie Mae's house to show off her engagement ring to her sisters.

When Horace Lee and Christine arrived at Fannie Mae's house, the rest of the family was seated around the living room. Christine walked in with her right hand covering her left hand. She sat down on the sofa between Rosalie and Marshall with her left hand still covered. She was just waiting for the right moment to reveal her diamond ring.

Marshall was being loud, inquisitive, outrageous, and so very wrong as usual. In a high-pitched screeching voice, which sounded like a disturbed peacock, he finally asked, "Why are you sitting here like you're hiding some of Miss Fannie Mae's silver stuck up under your dress?" With three snaps of his fingers high up in the air in a circular motion, he screamed, "Come on, Miss Thang, let me see what you got there?"

After Marshall kept cackling and repeatedly tugging at her right hand, Christine finally submitted to his intrusions and uncovered her left hand to reveal her diamond engagement ring.

"Horace Lee and I got engaged at his parents' house this evening," she replied demurely.

The sisters including Nettie all gathered around to see. Marshall gave a cross-eyed look at Horace Lee and asked, "Why are you buying this old heifer cow when you already done drunk all her milk? I'm sure her tits are all dried up and shriveled by now!" He made sucking noises with his lips.

Horace Lee ignored his future nephew-in-law. Belle, Rosalie, Nettie and Elenora all beamed with pride that Christine would finally be marrying Horace Lee. Fannie Mae got her wish even though she was not there in person — she was certainly there in spirit.

Through all of the commotion and celebration, Marshall suggested that they get married on Saturday, February 14, 2009, St. Valentine's Day. Everyone agreed that it would be a perfect day for a wedding. Without being asked, Marshall volunteered to be the wedding planner. Just like his mother, Rosalie, he had a way of inserting himself like an exclamation mark where it didn't belong. Together they agreed that the color scheme would be red and white in honor of Cupid's holiday. Belle volunteered to search through the boxes of dress patterns that she and Fannie Mae had been collecting for a cocktail-length wedding dress and bridesmaid dresses. With the help of Nettie, Rosalie and Elenora, she could have the dresses made in time. Christine asked her brother-in-law Esau Tate to give her away during the ceremony. Horace Lee asked Joe Bamo to be one of his groomsmen. It would be a family affair with Marshall Tate in charge and overseen by the spirit and memory of Fannie Mae Turner. They would ask Pastor Hicks to officiate the ceremony at New Ebenezer First Missionary Baptist Church. The wedding plans were now in motion.

The next day, the Turner sisters and Marshall drove up to Hancock Fabrics in Warner Robins, Georgia. Under the direction of the "wedding planner," they purchased yards and yards of Bordeaux Midnight Red fabric for the four bridesmaids' dresses, Candlelight White Duchesse Peau de Soie for Christine's dress, and Candlelight White Ming Brocade for her jacket. Marshall also picked out crystal beading for the neckline of Christine's dress. The next stop was Factory Brand Shoes at the Peach Shops in Byron, Georgia. There they purchased five pairs of white satin pumps, four of which would be dyed to match the bridesmaids' dresses.

When it came to the men, Marshall knew exactly how he wanted them to look — after all, he always imagined what his own wedding to the man of his dreams would be like. With a flick of his wrist and with his long tongue darting in and out of his mouth between puckered lips, he instructed Horace Lee to get himself and his groomsmen fitted for rental tuxedos at the Men's Wearhouse in Macon. Marshall sashayed back and forth as he described to Horace Lee exactly what he wanted them to wear. He recommended for the groom a black three-button tuxedo with white shirt, vest and bow tie. For the groomsmen, he suggested a merlot-colored dinner jacket with matching cummerbund and bow tie, black tuxedo pants and white shirt. The look would be simple and elegant, not the usual outlandish vision of Marshall Tate.

"I want y'all big ole handsome, sexy black men to be just ghetto fabulous," he shrieked.

As the wedding planner, he decided that he would wear his winter-white suit, red patent-leather slip-ons with white topstitching, and his brightest red-silk scarf. He told his father, Esau Tate, to wear his burgundy-colored three-piece suit to give the bride away.

"Daddy, make sure you don't ruin your only good suit when you is walking Christine down the aisle; you'll need it when I become the next bride in this family," said Marshall. "I'm catching the bouquet at the wedding, those bitches better stand back," he warned teasingly.

His father just smiled broadly and lowered his head in silence. Marshall knew just what buttons to push and how to embarrass his father. He kissed his father on his bowed forehead and strutted away.

The wedding party was all set for Christine and Horace Lee's Valentine's Day wedding.

In addition to Pastor Hicks officiating at the wedding ceremony, his wife, Ethel, volunteered to handle the floral arrangements for the church, bridal bouquets, and groom and groomsmen's flowers. She would also supervise the wedding reception decorations. This all would be done in accordance with Marshall's direction and oversight. He trusted Ethel Hicks to carry out his ideas in exact detail. She took notes as fast as she could as Marshall rattled off his list of floral demands at a rapid-fire pace.

"You got that all down, Sister Girl?" he asked as he dismissed her with a wave of his hand.

Marshall personally took care of the wedding invitations. He designed two interlocking white hearts with red lettering. The invitation requested that the guests wear red and white for Valentine's Day. He had a friend who owned a printing business in Albany who would print the invitations. This particular man was also one of his married sexual partners on the "down-low," a code name for men who had wives or girlfriends but engaged with other men sexually. Marshall expected that he would get a good deal on the printing costs.

His aunt Christine's wedding would be the fantasy wedding that Marshall Tate always dreamed of for himself. As a boy, he used to fantasize that he was the bride and that his next-door neighbor Derrick Taylor — Marshall's first crush — was the groom. When Derrick's mother caught them playing out this make-believe fantasy, she stopped the two boys from playing together unsupervised. Eventually, Derrick discovered girls and left Marshall completely devastated and heartbroken. When Derrick was killed in the Iraq War, Marshall mourned as if he was the widow left behind. For a whole month, he exchanged his bright colors for all-black clothing. While Rosalie and Esau knew why, they never questioned their son's odd behavior. They had come to expect almost anything from their only child at anytime.

CHAPTER 12

A PATTERN OF DECEIT (MY SISTER'S KEEPER)

Belle got busy taking measurements for Christine's wedding ensemble and for the bridesmaids' dresses for herself, Nettie, Rosalie and Elenora. She planned to train the other three in pattern cutting. Belle, with the help of her good friend from church Adele Hammond, intended to handle the assembling and sewing of the dresses. Elenora was chosen as Christine's maid of honor. This was an appropriate selection since the two of them had shared so much together as girls growing up. Elenora was always the recipient of Christine's hand-me-down clothes. The two had remained close until Elenora was suddenly sent away to New York to live with Fannie Mae's distant cousin Martha. Suspecting that the worst had happened to her baby sister, Christine felt guilty that she did not do more to protect her from John Henry Johnson.

Elenora was so self-centered, self-involved and strong-willed. She would never have listened to anyone who tried to stand in the way of what she wanted. And, she wanted John Henry Johnson in the worst way. Christine was disappointed when Elenora did not answer the many letters that she had written to her in care of Cousin Martha. Christine felt hurt and abandoned by her lack of communication. Elenora only wrote to her mother, Fannie Mae, and that was very infrequently. Now as the maid of honor in Christine's wedding, she would have the opportunity to redeem herself with her family and the community that she left behind.

Rosalie, Esau and Marshall Tate headed back to their life in Albany. They promised to return as often as necessary to help with the wedding plans. Marshall had already made arrangements for the reception hall, photographer and the wedding cake. Esau promised that he would bring his wife and son back to Oglethorpe to continue helping the other Turner sisters get ready for the happy occasion, considering the fact that they had just lost their beloved Fannie Mae. He was a dutiful husband, father, brother-in-law and son-in-law. Fannie Mae and Henry Turner were so proud when he married Rosalie and joined their family. They knew that Rosalie would be a handful for Esau, but they also knew that he would be a wonderful husband for her. And, he was. There was not another man in all of South Georgia who would have dared to put up with her obnoxious behavior.

The wedding reception was scheduled to be held at the Meade-Brown Mansion in Montezuma. The pre-Civil War Greek Revival mansion had been lovingly restored by Tom Meade III, grandson of Tom Meade who had owned the Oglethorpe General Store, and his life partner, Robert Steven Brown, grandson of Robert Brown who had owned the land adjacent to Christine's grandparents, Buck and Jesse Jessup. Rebecca Murray Pope, granddaughter of the former Macon County Sheriff Mack Murray, was hired as the wedding photographer. These three persons who would be playing a significant role in Christine and Horace Lee's wedding were direct descendents of men who were believed to have figured prominently in the disappearance of Buck Jessup back in 1927. Here it was two generations later and the mystery of Fannie Mae's father was still unsolved. Things had changed in Oglethorpe, Georgia and Macon County and yet they still remained the same!

Deloris Ellison, a member of New Ebenezer First Missionary Baptist Church, was commissioned to make a white three-tiered, heart shaped cake with red piping and red roses. Deloris made just about every cake for just about every wedding that took place in Macon County, black or white. She was considered to be the black Sylvia Weinstock of South Georgia. Just like the famous Sylvia Weinstock, Deloris' cakes were custom designed and one-of-a-kind. She never made the same cake twice. Each bride knew that a cake made for her special day by Deloris Ellison would be hers and hers alone.

Deloris also was widely known to have made cakes for no charge for deserving brides who could not afford to buy one. She aimed to please even for those on a tight budget. And, she made their cakes with the same meticulous attention to detail and loving care. While custom wedding cakes were her forte, she also made cakes for just about any occasion. Deloris once made a cake that was a replica of the plaque dedicated to the Lumpkin Academy at the intersection of Highway 49 and Ashbury Road in Oglethorpe, Georgia. Joe Bamo and Nettie could see the plaque from their kitchen window.

The Lumpkin Academy was established by Horace Lumpkin, Sr. as a private school for Negro boys in Macon County, Georgia. The academy provided an opportunity for them to receive a quality, first-rate education. Due to racial segregation they could not attend any other schools in the county. Deloris Ellison's cake commemorated this important period in Oglethorpe's black history.

Christine and Horace Lee had to return to Atlanta until just before their wedding in Oglethorpe. Before leaving, Horace Lee asked his brother, Bobby Lee Miller, to be his best man and his childhood friends Royce Jenkins and Cleophus Jones to join Joe Bamo as groomsmen. Christine asked her future sister-in-law, Carrie Lee Miller, to serve as wedding hostess. She cautioned her not to confuse her role with that of the wedding planner Marshall Tate. If she did, fur would fly! Carrie Lee got the message loud and clear. She had already heard about the infamous Marshall and knew that he would not take kindly to any such confusion. Carrie Lee would be no match for him. She would do everything possible to steer clear of Marshall Tate, the wedding planner.

Nettie and Joe Bamo returned to their quiet-and-peaceful lifestyle across the road from the Oglethorpe cemetery. They went back to business as usual, except now they would be keeping a watchful eye over Fannie Mae's gravesite. It was wintertime, so there would be no fishing at least for awhile. But, despite their life of peaceful solitude, they both were looking forward to Christine and Horace Lee's wedding. It was the first time that they were ever included in an event of this magnitude, except for church homecomings and picnics. They would be a part of the wedding party on the happiest day of Christine's life.

Elenora "Girlie" Turner settled into her new life back in Oglethorpe, Georgia. She began putting her identity and personal touches on Fannie Mae's house. She was so happy and relieved to be back at home again. Over the years and many times, she thought of coming back to Macon County and facing the truth, facing her true reality. However, she was concerned that she would bring shame upon her family, especially her dear mother, Fannie Mae. At the time that she left home she was pregnant with John Henry Johnson's child. Her sudden disappearance from Oglethorpe added fuel to the firestorm of rumors swirling around about her condition as well as the possibility that she and John Henry were also half-siblings. Both of their families were under a veil of suspicion, secrecy and speculation. Now that she was older she would stand up to anyone who dared to cross her. She had sacrificed enough over the years not being near her family, especially her darling mother, Fannie Mae, and her sisters. She would now make up for lost time.

The last time that Elenora returned to Macon County was for her father's funeral back in 1992, she briefly saw John Henry Johnson. He was the only member of his family in attendance at

Henry Turner's funeral. After the funeral, he came back to the Turner house to pay his respects. Elenora agreed to go for a drive with John Henry at his request. He apologized for the shame, pain, heartache and embarrassment that she had endured while he was able to remain a free man in Oglethorpe and continue on with his life as usual. He admitted that it was always easier on the boys in these circumstances, and that the girls were treated like outcasts. John Henry also admitted that it did not matter to him if he were Henry Turner's son, he would have loved her anyway. As far as he was concerned he only knew one father and that father was Calvin Johnson. That admission made her respect and love John Henry even more. At that moment she wished that she had really had a brother just like him.

The Turner and Johnson children were always very close schoolmates when they were growing up. In high school, John Henry and Elenora started dating against her parents' wishes. Despite the rumors about John Henry's true paternity, the two of them continued their relationship resulting in her pregnancy. Without warning, her parents put her on a Greyhound bus headed to New York City.

After having an abortion under the guardianship of her mother's distant cousin Martha, Elenora remained in New York City. Fannie Mae wanted her youngest daughter to return home to Oglethorpe and all would be forgiven, but Henry Turner felt differently; he felt that she should stay put where she was — and that would be the best for everyone involved.

Now here she was back in Macon County and both of her parents were now gone. She made a vow to herself that she would restore pride and honor to the name Elenora "Girlie" Turner. All that mattered was that her sisters had welcomed her back home without ever asking questions or even judging her. She was proud to be the daughter of Henry and Fannie Mae Turner, and that was all that really mattered. She decided that from now on she would only look forward and never look back on the past. She was thrilled that Christine had asked her to be the maid of honor in her wedding. This was a new beginning and a fresh start to their estranged relationship. When they were girls growing up she and Christine were the closest of all of the Turner sisters. Christine always protected her baby sister at school and made her feel safe and secure. Now she had the chance to return the favor. She would make sure that she was the best darn maid of honor any bride could ever hope for.

On the way back to Atlanta, Horace Lee and Christine stopped in at the Men's Wearhouse in Macon so that he could be fitted for his wedding tuxedo. Bobby Lee Miller, Cleophus Jones and Joe Bamo followed them in a separate car so that they could be fitted for their tuxedos as well. Christine got a sneak preview of what her husband-to-be and his groomsmen would look like on the day of their wedding. It was especially fun for Joe Bamo to be among other males and to take part in male bonding and a rite of passage. When he and Nettie got married, it was in her parents' living room with only family members present. Fannie Mae prepared the wedding supper. Their wedding ceremony was as quiet as their marriage. During the stopover in Macon, Christine saw another side of her brother-in-law. Joe Bamo seemed to come out of his quiet shell. He laughed and joked with the other men and seemed to genuinely enjoy their company. Christine was happy that her wedding to Horace Lee was bringing about positive changes within her entire family. Fannie Mae would be so proud.

CHAPTER 13

PLANNING A WEDDING (RED BORDEAUX AND CANDLELIGHT)

The wheels were in full-on motion for Christine and Horace Lee's wedding. The Turner sisters and Marshall were on track to meet their deadline. All of the dress patterns had been cut and pinned. It was two weeks before the wedding, and the day for the final fittings for the bride and bridesmaids at Elenora's new home. It seemed only appropriate that the fittings would take place in the house that was once Fannie Mae's. Her five daughters would all be together under her roof, giggling and laughing, trying on their dresses and just being Miss Fannie Mae's girls.

Horace Lee and Christine drove down from Atlanta. Esau, Rosalie and Marshall came up from Albany. Horace Lee's sister, Carrie Lee, and his mother, Hortense, drove over from Ellaville just to give moral support and to get better acquainted with their future in-laws. After Nettie and Joe Bamo arrived, Horace Lee took all of the men, except for Marshall, over to Ellaville to hang out with his father, Sam, and brother, Bobby Lee, to get acquainted in advance of the next day's Super Bowl party at the Miller's home. It was also a perfect opportunity to get away from all of the girlie wedding talk. He would leave Marshall and the women to sort through all things related to the upcoming nuptials. Like most grooms, Horace Lee would be just like any other guest at his own wedding. It would be all about the bride on her big day. It would be all about Christine. All he had to do was show up and get married.

It was Carrie Lee Miller's suggestion that her parents host a Super Bowl party for both families and the other members of the wedding party, Cleophus Jones and Royce Jenkins. This would be sort of a pre-wedding social event allowing for both families to relax and to get acquainted. This was also a perfect opportunity for Joe Bamo to relax around the other men involved in the wedding. He was unaccustomed to large groups of people outside of the Turner family. And, he was a bit uncomfortable and out of his element when it came to social gatherings altogether.

Marshall had arrived in Oglethorpe with his wedding planner's checklist. He was not only a wedding coordinator and organizer he was a real wedding choreographer. Christine and Horace Lee's wedding would be choreographed just like a Broadway musical. He had every detail and aspect right down to the "something borrowed and something blue." Anita Robinson, who sang at Fannie Mae's funeral, was asked to sing their favorite love songs, Whitney Houston's "I Will Always Love You," Jeffrey Osborne's "On The Wings of Love," and Roberta Flack's "The First Time Ever I Saw Your Face."

Marshall also had a sketch of the wedding cake that Deloris Ellison had emailed to him for his and Christine's approval. He had described the cake to Deloris in exact-and-vivid detail. That was easy for him to do since it was the very same cake design that he had imagined as a kid for his wedding to his next door neighbor Derrick. She had taken his vision and turned it into an artistic masterpiece. The entire gathering was in awe of her talent and could not wait to see the real thing.

Deloris had also designed a groom's cake for Horace Lee. His cake would be a red-velvet cake, a southern staple and by far his favorite. The groom's cake would be a replica of his football idol's jersey: former Atlanta Falcons Michael Vick's num ber seven. Horace Lee remained a loyal fan even after Michael Vick was disgraced, convicted and imprisoned in 2007 on federal charges of illegal dog fighting using pit bulls. Horace Lee refused to attend any more Falcons games and would not accept or acknowledge Matt Ryan as their new quarterback. He was a diehard Vick fan and nothing could change his mind. He would be so pleased with his groom's cake created by Deloris Ellison.

Since camellias were so popular in the region, Ethel Hicks went to the American Camellia Society headquarters at Massee Lane in Fort Valley, Georgia to decide which would be the best color matches for the fabric swatches that Belle had given her. She was amazed at the wide range of colors and varieties. For the bridesmaids she decided on a bouquet of deep red-velvet camellias with one white camellia in the center. Christine's bouquet for the bridal toss would be the exact opposite, full of white camellias with one deep-red velvet in the center. Her actual bridal bouquet would be made of fresh-cut flowers in the same design. The camellia leaves were a vivid shiny green and made for a very elegant bouquet, especially with baby's breath added in.

With the color scheme firmly in mind she continued on to Michael's Arts and Crafts in Warner Robins to meet with their floral designer. He was such a master artist he would be able to create the bouquets using silk flowers in the same color combinations. While there she also ordered the table centerpieces for the reception at Meade-Brown Mansion and the flower arrangements for the sanctuary at New Ebenezer First Missionary Baptist Church. The floral designer recommended burgundy-and-white silk orchids in glass vases surrounded by white votive candles for the wedding reception centerpieces and bunches of long-stemmed, burgundy-and-white roses for the sanctuary. Ethel Hicks also picked up the bridesmaids gifts, heart-shaped sterling-silver measuring spoons in red velvet boxes tied together with white silk organza ribbons. As a special token for such a generous purchase the floral designer gave her four white-and-burgundy silk orchid hair clips for the bridesmaids to wear in their hair. She would send the church van to pick up the floral order on the day before the wedding. Meanwhile, the floral designer offered to email her pictures of the completed bouquets and floral arrangements to show to Marshall and Christine for final approval.

Marshall met with the catering director of Meade-Brown Mansion, Beverly Alexander, to discuss the menu selection for the wedding reception. After going over many options, Marshall finally decided to honor his grandmother Fannie Mae Turner by having them prepare her southern-style Sunday supper. Rather than the traditional fancy foods that were normally served at Meade-Brown Mansion, the guests at the wedding reception for Mr. and Mrs. Horace Lee Miller would be served baked hen and dressing, cornbread, collard greens, yellow squash and pole beans. For dessert, they would have a choice of rice, banana, and bread puddings, and, of course, Deloris Ellison's delicious wedding cake served with fresh-brewed coffee and sweet iced tea.

Beverly Alexander tried to persuade Marshall to rethink his menu decision. She was more concerned about the reputation of Meade-Brown Mansion, known for its gourmet foods, rather than the wishes of her client. He could not and would not be swayed. Once again, Fannie Mae's grandson had done her proud.

Rosalie brought the pairs of shoes with her that had been dyed at a local shoe shop in Albany to match the color of the dresses for the bridesmaids. The owner of the shop was able to match the Bordeaux Midnight Red color exactly. He had often dyed shoes for Rosalie and Marshall to match their outrageous pastels. Unbeknownst to Rosalie, he was also one of her son Marshall's secret lovers on the down-low. Little did she know that besides the printer and the cobbler, he had also been with the butcher, baker and the candlestick maker. Marshall Tate had made the rounds of the local merchants in Albany.

The trying on of the bridesmaid's dresses was as much fun as the sisters used to have when they were young and living under Fannie Mae and Henry Turner's roof all together. Marshall beamed with pride at how much his fashion sense had really paid off. His keen eye in selecting the fabrics was right on target. Belle and Adele did a remarkable job in updating the old Butterick bridesmaid dress pattern that came from Fannie Mae's attic. They altered the lines to give the dresses a modern flair except for the maid of honor dress for Elenora. Her dress was actually backdated to reflect her love for 1960s Hollywood glamour styles. Her dress had a cinched waist and a pencil skirt to show off her gorgeous curves. Each bridesmaid's dress fit perfectly. All of the women congratulated Belle and Adele for a job that was done with such expertise. Who knew that there was so much dressmaking talent going on in little, old Oglethorpe, Georgia? Then came the moment that they all had been waiting for; it was time for Christine to try on her wedding suit that had been so lovingly created for her by her oldest sister, Belle. Once again Marshall's choice of fabric was right on target. The elegant combination of the Candlelight White Ming Brocade jacket over the sleek white sheath dress made from Candlelight White Duchesse Peau de Soie captured his fairy-tale vision just as he had imagined it. The addition of the crystal beading at the neckline and the white pillbox hat with a short veil made Christine look like a black Jacqueline Bouvier Kennedy or Grace Kelly. It was truly a radical transformation and departure from the polyester track suits that she normally wore to match Horace Lee's. Fannie Mae was somewhere in heaven smiling down upon her Princess Christine.

Her sister Elenora had applied a trial run of Christine's wedding-day makeup with the flair of a makeup artist. Elenora discovered an inexpensive imported cosmetic line while she was living in New York City. She found some products that were made in Milan, Italy to be a luxury cosmetic brand of the highest quality yet with an affordable price point. Since she was mostly an unemployed actress, she could not afford the more expensive brands. These products gave her the same glamour looks for less. On Christine's eyes, she blended a light application of Stardust Pearl eye shadow powder in with shades called Moon and Dark Violet. This gave her eyelids a luminous pearlescent glow that looked like a rose peeking through a harvest moon. She framed her eyes with smudge-proof Rum Raisin eyeliner. On Christine's lips she used an Intensity lipstick in Desert Rose topped with a thin veneer of clear lip gloss. Her lips were lined with a kiss-proof lip liner in the color of Bourdeaux Wine. Christine's medium-brown skin provided the perfect palette for the cosmetic shades and colors. The rest of the bridal party could not wait until Elenora applied their makeup on the wedding day. Miss Fannie Mae's girls would be five pretty maidens all in a row.

With the upcoming nuptials of Horace Lee Miller and Christine Turner, the family was uncovering all sorts of hidden talents. Marshall Tate had become a wedding planner beyond compare, especially in these parts of South Georgia. His aunt Belle had shown her talents as an expert designer and dressmaker and his aunt Elenora wowed everyone as a makeup artist. Perhaps, there could be a bridal business in their future?

CHAPTER 14

MEET THE MILLERS, IT'S A SUPER SUNDAY

Super Bowl Sunday, February 1, 2009, followed the day after the final dress fitting for Christine Turner and her bridesmaids. Horace Lee's family invited the entire bridal party to watch the Super Bowl at their home. This gathering was a prelude to the big day when Horace Lee Miller and Christine Turner would tie the knot on Valentine's Day, Saturday, February 14, 2009.

Yet Cupid's arrow had pierced their hearts long before he asked her to marry him. They started living together in Atlanta almost immediately after they met at Bigelow's Bar and Grill. Christine was far away from her mother, Fannie Mae, and from the prying, watchful eyes of small town Oglethorpe, Georgia. She was free to live her life as she pleased. What she did not know was that her mother knew about her and Horace Lee living in sin for quite some time before they ever went public. Fannie Mae, on a very rare occasion, had called Christine just because she was on her mind. When Horace Lee answered the telephone, she hung up without saying anything. Fannie Mae was certain that she had dialed the correct number, but dialed it again just to be sure. The same male voice answered. The next time she heard from Christine, she never revealed her suspicions. Her daughter was a grown woman supporting herself. She decided not to interfere in her life — she would only pray harder for her.

Sam and Hortense Miller and their three children, Horace Lee, Bobby Lee and Carrie Lee, hosted the Super Bowl party. The guests included Belle Turner, her friend Adele Hammond, Joe and Nettie Bamo, Esau, Rosalie and Marshall Tate, Christine Turner, Elenora Turner, Cleophus Jones and Royce Jenkins. Esau Tate and Joe Bamo had visited with Horace Lee the day before, so they were already ahead in getting acquainted. This gathering reflected the entire wedding party and marked the beginning of the merger of two families. The Millers wanted to be the best hosts and to please the Turners. Likewise, the Turners wanted to make a good impression on the Miller family. Belle warned Marshall and Rosalie to be on their best behavior just as Fannie Mae would have done. All they could do was hope and pray for a miracle. It was anybody's guess how the two renegades from Albany would behave.

Samuel Miller had prepared his slow-cooked Texas-style chili and his pit-cooked, chopped barbecue for sandwiches. His wife made southern-style potato salad and coleslaw. Carrie Lee cooked spicy buffalo wings and made deviled eggs. Horace Lee was responsible for the beverages. Since the game was between the Pittsburgh Steelers and the Arizona Cardinals, he purchased three cases of Iron City Beer from a distributor in Atlanta and two cases of assorted flavors of Arizona Iced Teas from Costco. The ice-cold Iron City Beer provided the perfect complement for the spicy chili and barbecue sandwiches. The Arizona teas would surely draw objections from southern sweet-tea enthusiasts and purists who would never drink tea from a bottle, but still it was a thoughtful tribute to the Arizona Cardinals even though it was manufactured in New York.

When Rosalie saw the bottles of iced tea in the large tin tub with the Iron City Beer, she cleared her throat and asked Hortense Miller, "Don't they sell tea bags over here in Ellaville, Georgia? This is South Georgia not South Philly!"

Hortense had been warned about Rosalie and Marshall by Horace Lee, so she just smiled sweetly and said, "Sugar, I can make you some fresh brewed tea if you like." She remembered that her own mother used to tell her, "You can catch more flies with honey than with vinegar."

Rosalie was stunned that her insult had landed with a thud. Her face, already the color of red Georgia clay, got even redder. She could already see that her acerbic wit would not play well in the Miller household.

No one attending the Miller's party had a particular favorite in Super Bowl XLIII. Most of the men, however, rooted for Pittsburgh; the women and Marshall favored Arizona because of Kurt Warner's sexy good looks. They found him to be more appealing than Ben Roethlisberger.

Marshall jumped up and screamed with pom-poms waving from side to side like a high-school cheerleader whenever his quarterback took the field. He randomly commented with statements such as:

"Ain't he just something pretty and delicious?"

"I could just eat him up!"

"That Kurt Warner is just fine as frog's hair."

The Turners had grown accustomed to his outbursts; but he was a bit much, a curiosity for the Millers and the two other groomsmen, Cleophus Jones and Royce Jenkins. Everyone eventually found him to be quite entertaining and amusing, especially when he thought his team was making a good play even when it was not. To these folks from South Georgia, Marshall was far more entertaining than Bruce Springsteen at halftime. They all came to like the odd-and-queer fellow from Albany and could not wait until the wedding day to see more of his antics.

During the game, it became apparent that Elenora and Royce Jenkins were really hitting it off. She acted coy and demure as if she was playing a part on Broadway. She was the lead actress as she tried to set a trap to catch her leading man. Elenora batted her false eyelashes and fanned herself with a lace handkerchief like a southern belle with the vapors on a hot summer's day. In a manner of speaking, she was "setting her hat for her beau." All of these theatrics drew his attention first to her body and then to her cleavage. Royce found her to be very stylish, intriguing and interesting, considering the fact that she was from Macon County, Georgia. She fascinated him with her tales of life in New York City. She, on the other hand, thought that he was just a little too country for her tastes, but charming all the same.

Whenever he went for food or a beverage, she would ask him to bring her something as well. This mutual admiration and attraction did not go unnoticed by the others. Marshall kept rolling his eyes and snapping his fingers in the air at his aunt Elenora whenever Royce left the room.

"You go, girl!" he said to encourage her.

She tried to ignore him, but he would not let her escape his scrutiny. The other Turner sisters wondered if Elenora just might find true love in South Georgia after all — especially since John Henry Johnson was no longer a possible suitor; however, a platonic relationship might still develop between them. Enough time had passed and only time would tell.

Nettie and Joe Bamo seemed to come out of their quiet shells. She was very talkative with Hortense and Carrie Lee, and he spent time talking to Sam Miller. He also talked with Bobby Lee and Cleophus, who he had driven up to the Men's Wearhouse in Macon with for their tuxedo fittings. Elenora otherwise had occupied Royce's time. For Joe Bamo, this was the beginning of his bonding with other males outside of his brother-in-law Esau and his wife's nephew Marshall — a major breakthrough for him. He showed another side of himself that Nettie and the other Turner sisters had not seen before.

While all of the other women and Marshall had fun pretending to be interested in the Super Bowl, they were more interested in discussing the upcoming wedding. They talked about the wedding dresses that Belle and Adele had made. Marshall made sure that everyone knew that the fabric choice was his and his alone.

"I could be the next Vera Wang," he shrieked.

"Vera who?" the others asked almost in unison.

"You know that Chinese woman who designs those pretty, expensive wedding dresses for famous folks?" Marshall replied.

They all stared at him with puzzled looks on their faces as he continued, "Just call me Marshall Thang."

Everyone laughed as if they knew who and what he was talking about.

He also let it be known that he had designed every single detail of the wedding and the reception. "I could put that David Tutera to shame," he said as a reference to the famous wedding planner to the stars.

Once again there were blank stares on their faces, but they decided it best to not even ask Marshall to explain, at the risk of sounding dumb.

The wedding talk went on despite the fact that the Super Bowl was in progress. At least until Horace Lee's ex-girlfriend Priscilla Jenkins arrived unannounced. Royce's sister had stopped by the Miller's home under the guise of having something important to tell her brother. Carrie Lee invited her to come in and then warned the other women and Marshall of the backstory behind Horace Lee and Priscilla.

"She and Horace Lee used to date. She got pregnant on purpose, trying to trap him into marrying her. She lost the baby, and he moved up to Atlanta to go to college," Carrie Lee whispered almost all in one breath.

She begged them not to repeat a word of it in front of Priscilla, especially Marshall — and that request was like talking to a fence post.

"Say what? She did what? Ooh child! Hush your mouth," screamed Marshall before his mother, Rosalie, could put her hand over his mouth.

Carrie Lee assured Christine that her brother had absolutely no interest in Priscilla anymore. Just to make sure, Marshall promised to protect his aunt Christine's interest by keeping the interloper occupied.

"Leave her to me," he told Christine.

He immediately complimented Priscilla on her long-flowing, two-toned black-and-red hair-weave. "I wants me some hair like yours girlfriend!" he said as he tossed his head from side to side in sweeping motions touching his temples with his fingertips. He also mocked her tight blue jeans. "Did you use Crisco to slide your big hips into those pants, Miss Thing?"

Priscilla did not know whether to take him seriously, or if he was just joking. He was on a roll and just would not quit. Poor Priscilla could not get a word in.

"Your brother Royce is just so fine. I had my eyes on him before Elenora 'Girlie' Brown latched on to him," he continued. "Do you have another brother at home who's fine like him?"

Carrie Lee rescued her from Marshall's verbal clutches and guided her to safety. Priscilla decided not to stick around for more of the same. She beat a hasty retreat without ever talking to her brother Royce or congratulating Horace Lee on his upcoming wedding — and for breaking her heart.

After having met Marshall Tate, wedding planner extraordinaire of Albany, Georgia, Carrie Lee could not wait to see him in action on the wedding day. She knew that her role as hostess would be simply overshadowed by his powerful and colorful personality. She would just do as the "man" in charge told her.

After the Pittsburgh Steelers pulled off the win with less than three minutes to go to beat the Arizona Cardinals 27-23, Marshall faked tears in support of his losing quarterback Kurt Warner. Warner's wife would certainly not be flattered. The party broke up shortly after the end of the game. The Turners, Bamos and Tates thanked the Millers for their hospitality and excellent party food.

Hortense Miller hugged them all and said, "Goodbye," and told them that the two families would have more gatherings between Ellaville and Oglethorpe.

Elenora told Royce Jenkins that he did not have to wait for a wedding to visit her in Oglethorpe. She added that the door would be open and the welcome mat out at Miss Fannie Mae's house.

He got the message loud and clear.

Belle said to the Millers that she looked forward to seeing them at the wedding rehearsal and dinner following in the church hall at New Ebenezer First Missionary Baptist Church.

Marshall told everyone to be at the church at 6:00 p.m. sharp on Friday the 13th. He made a point of telling Bobby Lee Miller, Royce Jenkins and Cleophus Jones, "Don't be late or you'll get a spanking from me!"

They all laughed and promised not to be late. Not one of them was interested in getting spanked by Marshall Tate of Albany, Georgia.

CHAPTER 15

LOVE IS HERE (HAIR IS GONE)

On Friday morning the 13th of February, Ethel Hicks sent Purvis and Percival Johnson with the church van up to Michael's Arts and Crafts in Warner Robins to pick up the wedding bouquets, floral arrangements for the sanctuary, and table centerpieces and votive candles for the wedding reception at Mead-Brown Mansion. On their return trip, they stopped by the mansion to deliver the items for the wedding reception to the catering director, Beverly Alexander.

Despite the fact that the centerpieces were made with silk flowers rather than fresh, she could not help but admire the sheer beauty and authenticity of the burgundy-and-white orchids in glass vases sprinkled with baby's breath. Once again, she considered the reputation and standards of Meade-Brown Mansion but quickly dismissed her lofty judgment. The flowers were simply elegant and very appropriate.

Beverly Alexander quickly became a convert to accepting silk flower arrangements. She was previously so adamant that she stated emphatically, "There will only be fresh flowers in Meade-Brown Mansion! There will be no exceptions!"

That edict changed once she met the formidable Marshall Tate, wedding planner extraordinaire from Albany, Georgia. "After all fresh flowers eventually die, silk lives on forever" was his response to her initial objections.

On the way down to Oglethorpe from Atlanta, Horace Lee stopped to pick up his tuxedo as well as the tuxedos for his best man and his groomsmen at the Men's Wearhouse in Macon. The salesman insisted that he try on his tuxedo to make sure that it was a perfect fit. It was extremely important that the groom's attire be impeccable and flawless. No one would care much if a groomsman had an ill-fitting tuxedo, but certainly not the groom.

Even though Horace Lee was in a hurry, he agreed to the fitting. Horace Lee was even more handsome in formal wear, especially since he had a neat new haircut. The Jheri-curl was gone. His friend Royce Jenkins had suggested that his hairstyle was outdated and that he should consider something much more current for his wedding. He took Royce's advice, and then wondered why he had not considered the change on his own. His new haircut made him look so much more polished and sophisticated.

When he walked into the barber shop on Hill Street in Atlanta, the barber he was referred to, Ira, took one look at Horace Lee's Jheri-curl and thought to himself, "Oh hell no!"

The other barbers were accustomed to seeing dreadlocks and "afros," but had not seen a Jheri-curl walk through the door in years. They tried to ignore this relic from the past, but it was hard. Their thoughts ranged from: "What the hell was he thinking?" to, "Get the hell out of here!"

Whenever Rosalie Tate saw Horace Lee and Christine with their matching gold teeth and Jheri-curls, she would whisper to her son, Marshall, "Ooh child, look at that mess!"

Ira politely welcomed Horace Lee to "Soul Scissors," led him to the shampoo bowl, and donned a pair of rubber gloves. After two vigorous shampoos, Horace Lee was ready for a new cut and style. When he left "Soul Scissors," he looked like a brand new man. Ira had given him a low, conservative cut that showed off his hair's natural wave pattern. Next he would probably consider having his gold teeth replaced.

Down in Oglethorpe the Turner sisters and Marshall had gathered at Fannie Mae's house. Even Elenora still found it hard not to call her new home "Mama's house." Marshall had hired a stylist friend from Albany to provide services to the bride and her wedding party. Jerome was a hairstylist and nail technician by day and "Neesha" the drag queen by night. He knew everything that there was to know about hair and nails and brought all the products necessary to transform their everyday drab looks into glamorous wedding hairdos and to make their stubby nails long and elegant. He was prepared to shorten or lengthen, lighten or darken, curl or straighten.

Jerome arrived with hairpieces, hair relaxers, curling irons, straightening combs, and a wide selection of semi-permanent hair colors. It was like "Steel Magnolias" except these were southern belles of color about to get ready for Oglethorpe's wedding of the year. He brought Fifth Avenue hairstyling to Macon County, Georgia.

The most amazing transformation created by Jerome was that of the bride-to-be Christine. He was quite frank, blunt and to the point much like Marshall would have been if she were not his aunt.

He simply told Christine, "This Jheri-curl has got to go, Miss Thing! Do you want that activator juice all over your beautiful wedding suit? I'm fixing to straighten this mess out. It just ain't healthy," he said as he ran his fingers through her hair.

Jerome washed her hair repeatedly to rid it of the activator and to loosen the curl pattern. He used his blow dryer to return her hair to a more natural texture, and then applied a heat-activated, deep-penetrating conditioner and placed her under a heat cap. Because he was very concerned about her many years of severe hair damage, rather than using a relaxer he simply used his incredible styling tools. Jerome straightened her hair with his flat iron. With the same iron, he made large fluffy curls and combed them in to the finished hairstyle.

Christine's hair was restored to the beautiful texture of her youth. The other women were amazed at his mastery and the art of hair design. They also remembered his alter-ego Neesha's beautiful hair at Fannie Mae's wake. Jerome would be back the next morning to provide the final touch up to the bride and bridesmaids' hair.

Over at the Meade-Brown Mansion, Tom Meade III, Robert Steven Brown, Beverly Alexander and their staff prepared the reception hall for the next day's festivities. The mansion was not only a venue-for-hire, it was also Tom and Robert's private home. Only the grounds, the foyer, lavatories and reception hall were open to the public. The staff set about arranging and decorating the head table for the bridal party and round tables for the guests. They draped the head table in white with red bunting, and draped the round tables with white tablecloths. They placed burgundy-and-white orchid centerpieces in glass vases surrounded by white votive candles in glass holders on each table. All of the sterling-silver eating utensils sat on red damask napkins. Marshall selected the white china pattern embossed with roses for the dinner and the head-table place settings. Two smaller side tables were draped in white for the wedding cake and groom's cake that Deloris Ellison would deliver on Saturday morning. They also set up two well-stocked bars on either side of the entrance from the main hall of the mansion.

Rebecca Murray Pope stopped by the Meade-Brown Mansion to see the setup for the Miller-Turner wedding reception and to block shots for the next day. She had photographed many wedding receptions in the grand hall as well as around the beautiful grounds of the mansion, but she always tried to capture a unique perspective for each event. When it came to weddings, she wanted each couple to have their very own lighting, mood and ambience. She had already done lighting checks over at New Ebenezer First Missionary Baptist Church and intended to return later in the evening for the wedding ceremony rehearsal and dinner.

The deejay hired by Marshall Tate, "Cool Curtis Mo D," set up his equipment in the reception hall and did a sound check. He used a playlist compiled of the greatest soul hits from the '60s through the '90s. He had something to please everyone. Marshall requested that he play three Sounds of Philadelphia hit songs, the Stylistics "You Make Me Feel Brand New" for the newlyweds first dance, Sister Sledge's "We Are Family" for the Turner sisters to dance to together, and the Intruders "I'll Always Love My Mama" for Horace Lee and his mother and dedicated to Fannie Mae Turner.

The ghosts of the pre-Civil War Meade-Brown Mansion in Montezuma, Georgia would be dancing in the walls and Tom Mead, Robert Brown and Mack Murray would be turning over in their graves. Buck Jessup, wherever his body had been hidden on that July night in 1927, would be turning over as well. His granddaughter Christine would be having her wedding reception at the mansion owned by the gay grandsons of two of his KKK assailants. The granddaughter of a third assailant would be documenting the whole event. As Rosalie Tate would probably say, "Ooh child, look what you get when you do ugly!"

CHAPTER 16

TAKE YOUR PLACES (WE'RE GOING TO HAVE A WEDDING)

When the Turner and Miller families and the other members of the wedding party arrived at New Ebenezer First Missionary Baptist Church for the wedding rehearsal, Pastor Hicks, Ethel Hicks, the organist-pianist Bertha Hightower, and soloist Anita Robinson greeted them. The bride and groom, Christine and Horace Lee, were also greeted by something new and unexpected — each other's new hairstyles. It was like they were meeting for the first time. Their fresh, modern and new looks made their eyes dance with delight at the sight of the person before them who they would marry the next day.

The Johnson twins, Purvis and Percival, had placed the floral arrangements on the altar of the sanctuary and had decorated the front family pews with large red bows and red-and-white streaming ribbons exactly as instructed. Marshall Tate with a keen eye inspected their work to ensure that each bow was tied exactly the same and that each of the ribbons were the exact same length. He felt pleased that they had followed his instructions and got it right. Meticulous and anal-retentive about the minutest details of the smallest things, Marshall held high standards for this special occasion.

Marshall gathered all of the women at the back of the sanctuary and all of the men at the front near the altar. He started the wedding rehearsal walk-through with Pastor Hicks, the groom and the groomsmen first. He assigned Cleophus Jones and Royce Jenkins to escort the wedding guests to their pews. After the hostess, Carrie Lee Miller, greeted the wedding guests, she would ask each of them to sign the guestbook; Cleophus would seat the bride's family and guests on one side of the church and Royce would seat the groom's side on the other. After all of the guests were seated, Joe Bamo would do a symbolic seating of the mother of the bride, Fannie Mae Turner. Since Fannie Mae had died a month and a half earlier, Joe Bamo would place a light-blue satin pillow with lace and embroidery with her name on it in the seat reserved for her.

"Uncle Joe, this is not a speaking part, you just walk that pretty, little pillow quietly down to the front of the church and place it just so," Marshall said as he demonstrated how to hold the pillow and sashay toward the front pew. "Think you can handle that?"

Joe Bamo looked at his nephew quizzically and wondered if he also needed to imitate the walk as well. He then headed down the aisle quite awkwardly, carefully placing one foot in front of the other with a slight sway. They all laughed, and Joe Bamo smiled back at them with beads of perspiration popping out all over his forehead.

"Now Fat Ethel, oops, I mean Mrs. Hicks," Marshall said apologetically with one hand covering his mouth after realizing his slip of the tongue. He had called her by her nickname, which was never used publicly, only in private, and only by those close to her.

She nodded with dignity almost as if she didn't even hear him.

"You will have the seat of honor on the bride's side right next to my grand mama's pillow," said Marshall. "Now Bobby Lee Miller, since you are the best man and brother of the groom, you will escort your mother, Hortense, to her seat first, followed by your sister, Carrie Lee, and then your father, Sam."

Marshall hooked his arm inside of Bobby Lee's, smiled at him adoringly and showed him how to walk his family members to their seats. Bobby Lee tensed as the two of them walked down the aisle together. Marshall's intimate touch made him nervous and shaky. He was relieved when Marshall let go of his arm and was much more relaxed when it finally came time to practice with his parents and sister. His sense of relief did not go unnoticed by the others.

"Horace Lee, after your parents have been seated, you and Pastor Hicks will enter the sanctuary from the pastor's study on the right side of the church and stand facing the rear of the church," said Marshall.

Horace Lee and Pastor Hicks easily followed the instructions — they were simple enough since there was no reason for

Marshall to show them how to walk through a door and how to stand; however, Marshall found the need to show them anyway. He positioned each of them on their marks. Clapping his hands wildly in the air and snapping his fingers to get their attention, he motioned and pointed to their places on the floor.

He told them, "Stand erect! Pretend that you are in the army, shoulders back, chests stuck out, tummies tucked in, and look straight ahead at me." Marshall barked off his commands at them as if they were in the military.

Marshall took both of his hands and pressed each of their stomachs until they were flat. Then he stood behind them and pulled on their shoulders until they both looked like thc Queen's Guard at Buckingham Palace. Neither person smiled; they only winced at being touched so personally and intimately by Marshall Tate. They were both happy to stand at-ease when he was done with them and began to next focus his attention onto the groomsmen.

Pastor Hicks said to Horace Lee, "I promise you that when you get married tomorrow, you might be a little nervous, but Marshall won't be standing here next to you. It will be your lovely bride touching you."

Horace Lee let out a sigh of relief.

Bobby Lee, Royce, Cleophus and Joe Bamo were instructed to march from the rear of the church forward to join Horace Lee on the right side of the altar in the same order with their bodies angled and to face the pews. In single file, they all stood at attention and made their way down the aisle. Marshall beamed with pride like a sergeant would over his new recruits. Recognizing his pleasure with them, they all smiled back at Marshall with big toothy grins.

Cleophus turned slightly and whispered in Royce's ear, "That was easier than I thought it would be."

Royce whispered back, "Yeah, I know. Still, he makes me so nervous, especially the way he keeps staring at my ass."

"Your ass and my package!" replied Cleophus.

Marshall gave them one nasty look that caused the whispers to stop instantly.

"I heard that!" he said. "As far as I can see, neither one of you have enough ass or package to get me excited!"

The two men hung their heads in shame, bashful by the fact that Marshall had placed them in a spotlight that they had no desire to be in. Marshall Tate's sharp tongue was not one to be fooled with, especially if you feared the deep end of the pool. Many had fallen victim and drowned under his sharp and witty nature, as well intentioned as it was.

Marshall's plans called for a non-traditional processional for the bridesmaids, the maid of honor and the bride. Rather than using traditional wedding marches, Anita Robinson would sing solo accompanied by Bertha Hightower. The bridesmaids and maid of honor would enter the sanctuary and walk forward from the rear of the church while Anita Robinson sang Jeffrey Osborne's "On the Wings of Love." Marshall would cue each one of them as to when she should start down the aisle to keep the appropriate spacing and pace with the music.

The sisters were all giggly and chattering as they followed his instructions, like when they were growing up in Henry and Fannie Mae's house.

"I wish Mama and Daddy could be here to see their little girl walk down the aisle," Belle said to Nettie.

"Yeah, I know they would be so proud of 'Sweetie Pie,'" Nettie responded gleefully and out loud, not in her usual quiet whisper of a voice.

Rosalie leaned forward to make sure that it was Nettie's voice that she was actually hearing.

"Girl, where did you get that big voice from?" Rosalie asked.

"It's been here all the time," replied Nettie as she turned around. "You just couldn't hear me because of your big ole mouth running all the time!"

They all laughed nearly falling into one another.

"Hush your mouth girl! Go on away from here!" Rosalie shouted back with both hands waving in the air.

"Now I do declare Miss Nettie Bamo!" hollered Elenora.

Marshall just put his hands on his hips and shook his head at his mother and his aunts, "Shush, y'all! You all better pay attention or you will be kicked out of your own sister's wedding. I mean it, you can be replaced in a heartbeat. I know some homeless women at the shelter down in Albany who would love to be in your dresses and walking in your pumps!" he continued.

They all laughed, ignoring his officious and impertinent behavior and continued on with their merriment. Elenora could not stop laughing at the fact that quiet Nettie Bamo finally stood up to "Big Red."

"You go, girl" she said to Nettie when she gained control of herself. "Ole Joe Bamo better watch out or he just might end up in that cemetery across the road from y'all!" Elenora continued.

Nettie smiled at her younger sister like Miss Celie smiled at Shug Avery in "The Color Purple." "Thank you, Miss Lena Turner!"

That brought a smile to Elenora's face.

Nettie had found her voice partly because her sister Elenora had returned home to Oglethorpe and decided to stay on. She now had a new ally, a new balance, and a leveled playing field to the family dynamic. When they came to visit from Albany, Rosalie and Marshall would no longer overshadow Nettie.

Belle would be the first to walk down the aisle, then Nettie, followed by Rosalie and Elenora. They would line up angled on the left side of the altar in that very same order with Belle the furthest from Pastor Hicks and Elenora the closest, leaving a space for Christine to join her groom, Horace Lee, at the altar.

Marshall led the promenade in order to show them exactly how to walk and what pace and distance to keep between them. He walked slowly with his hands clasped together in front of him, as if he were carrying a bouquet in his own imaginary wedding. Marshall turned his head ever so slightly from side to side as he strolled down the aisle.

"This is a wedding damn it, not a funeral! Act like it!" he shouted as his head moved in each direction.

He walked as if he were a contestant in the "Miss Black America" pageant and acknowledged all who had gathered to see him as he glided along the runway.

When the wedding party was all in place, Marshall gave

Purvis and Percival Johnson the cue to unfurl a long roll of paper instead of the actual red satin runner down the center aisle of the church. Marshall did not want to risk damaging the runner before the wedding the next day. After all, this was only the rehearsal and not the main event. He was afraid that Purvis and Percival in their efforts to please him would clumsily rip or tear the real runner. Just as he thought, the twins were nervous and jittery in his presence. Neither felt sure of when to step and when to unroll more of the paper.

"Come on Laverne and Shirley, get moving! These people came to see the bride and not you two fools!" Marshall scolded them, making them even more nervous.

The two of them moved hurriedly along and got out of the way quickly. When they were out of earshot of Marshall, Purvis and Percival looked at each other and said almost simultaneously as twins often do, "That is one ole crazy fool!"

Christine escorted by her brother-in-law Esau Tate would proceed down the aisle to meet her groom at the altar while Ms. Robinson sang Roberta Flack's "The First Time Ever I Saw Your Face."

As they began to walk down the aisle on cue from Marshall, Christine held tight to Esau's arm and said, "Thanks so much for always being such a good brother-in-law. Daddy and Mama were so happy when you and Rosalie got married, and now here you are walking me down the aisle. They would be so proud."

Esau just smiled and patted her hand on his arm, reassuring her that indeed her parents would be so proud of her as well.

As the rehearsal continued, Esau and Christine reached

the altar where Pastor Hicks asked, "Who gives this bride to this groom?"

Esau responded, "I do," and then presented Christine to Horace Lee. The two men shook hands, and Esau took his seat in the first pew next to Ethel Hicks. Before Pastor Hicks started the religious wedding ceremony in the traditional manner, he told Horace Lee to take Christine's hand. They faced one another and clasped each other's hands tightly.

Horace Lee whispered to Christine, "Today, you are my girl, tomorrow you will be my wife."

She smiled up and him and replied, "You'll always be my man."

The other wedding party members tried to lean in to hear what was being said, but to no avail.

Pastor Hicks then deferred to Christine and Horace Lee to recite their personal vows of love and commitment that they would be delivering to each other at their wedding on the following day. Pastor Hicks resumed the wedding ceremony rehearsal by pronouncing them man and wife and permitted Horace Lee to kiss his fiancée.

Marshall, who had been silent throughout this part, with tears in his eyes he finally said to the couple, "OK, Ike and Tina Turner, save that shit for tomorrow. You ain't married yet!"

The wedding rehearsal ended with the introduction of the new couple by Pastor Hicks, "I now give you Mr. and Mrs. Horace Lee Miller."

Ethel Hicks then placed a handmade straw broom down for the couple to do the African tradition of "jumping the broom."

Anita Robinson singing "I Will Always Love You" by Whitney Houston accompanied the recessional of the newlyweds, the bridesmaids and groomsmen locked arm in arm, followed by Pastor Hicks. The entire wedding party fell out of formation to gather around the bride- and groom-to-be. Everyone was glad that the rehearsal was over. Marshall had put them all through their paces; they applauded and shouted, "Hallelujah!"

The rehearsal of Marshall's well-coordinated and orchestrated wedding of his aunt Christine Turner to Horace Lee Miller was now complete. He was totally satisfied with the performance of everyone involved. Even though Purvis and Percival Johnson were nervous ninnies around the wedding coordinator, they were able to unroll the runner down the aisle without making any mistakes. Just the way that Marshall clapped his hands to get the wedding party's attention and to get them into position and on their marks was intimidating enough. Bobby Lee, Cleophus and Royce were too macho to show any fear, but deep down inside they knew not to cross the wedding planner. Marshall could smell their fear, and he played each one of them for his own amusement. Everyone had done their parts exactly as told and managed to ensure that the next day would go off without a hitch.

"Job well done, now let's eat," Marshall announced.

They all headed down to the church hall where the Women's Auxiliary of New Ebenezer First Missionary Baptist Church had prepared a rehearsal dinner feast. The tables in the church hall were arranged in a U-shape so that all of the bridal party and family members could interact and face each other.

The dinner was as Rosalie described it, "Ooh child, this food is holier than thou!"

The fixings included fried chicken, catfish, hush puppies, pig's feet, potato salad, collard greens, black-eyed peas, and cornbread. Dessert included banana pudding, red-velvet cake and pineapple-coconut cake. And of course, they served southern sweet tea.

Because the rehearsal dinner was held in the church, there were no alcoholic beverages served. However, Bobby Lee Miller, the best man, brought a speakeasy on wheels to make sure that his brother had a proper bachelor party of sorts. In the trunk of his car, he stored an ice chest with the leftover Iron City Beer from the Super Bowl party and bottles of Moonshine (corn liquor) that his daddy had made. The groom and groomsmen kept disappearing outside, leaving the others inside to talk about the upcoming wedding.

Rosalie soon caught on to what was going on and joined the men out in the church parking lot. "What's ya'll doing out here in the dark?" she hollered in her usual piercing voice.

"Shush," said Horace Lee.

Elenora and Marshall were not going to be left out either. When they went outdoors, they heard "PSST, over here!"

Rosalie called to her sister and her son who joined the group around the open trunk of Bobby Lee's car. Before long, Pastor Hicks, Purvis and Percival, Sam Miller and Esau joined in with the outdoor bachelor party. They were all huddled together and kept each other warm while downing shots of Moonshine.

Elenora and Royce Jenkins took a walk around the back of

the church to grab a private moment together. Their privacy did not last very long; Rosalie and Marshall soon followed them.

"What y'all got going on round here?" bellowed Rosalie.

"I knew you two had the fever for each other," added Marshall.

Elenora Turner and Royce Jenkins had been busted. The whole gathering outdoors started making cooing sounds and suggesting, "There ought to be a double wedding tomorrow."

Everyone cheered and egged the sneaky couple on. Truth be told, Elenora and Royce had been out on date already. Three days after meeting at the Super Bowl party, they went down to Americus to see a movie together. After Rosalie and Marshall blew their cover, they thought that they might as well go public.

During the rehearsal when Royce saw Elenora walk down the aisle in the processional of bridesmaids, for a fleeting moment he imagined that she was coming to join him in marriage. When he first saw her at the Miller's party on Super Bowl Sunday, he felt immediately drawn to her beauty and sophistication. She was so different than the other women that he had met in South Georgia. The many years that she had spent away from Oglethorpe had transformed her from a rural country girl into a cosmopolitan woman by Macon County standards. Royce became determined to pursue a casual relationship with Elenora to see where it might lead. He just might be the Porgy for her Bess. And would he be the Joe for her Carmen Jones? Only time would tell.

The rehearsal dinner turned bachelor party ended at about 11:00 p.m., with the men promising that they would get to the church on time the next day.

The five Turner sisters spent the night at Elenora's house. They all wanted to be together in sisterhood and to feel the spirit of Fannie Mae all around them on the night before Christine's big day. This was where they would get ready for the wedding the next day. Elenora would do their makeup, and Jerome or Neesha would arrive from Albany in the morning to touch up their hair. No one knew which one would come. Christine's wedding suit and the bridesmaids' dresses were all finished and pressed, hanging and waiting. They sat up talking and laughing most of the night.

Rosalie asked Christine, "Where are you and Horace Lee going for your honeymoon?"

Elenora chimed in, "Honeymoon? What honeymoon? They done had the honeymoon long before the wedding!"

Belle added, "He's already done drank that gal's milk; it was so good, now he's buying the cow."

Nettie just blushed and smiled at the bawdy behavior of her sisters. They all told Nettie that to overcome her shyness and stage fright at the wedding the next day, she should just imagine that everyone else at the wedding was naked. She blushed all over again.

Marshall and his father, Esau, stayed at Belle's house just through the clearing in the woods. Rosalie gave them bedtime orders and instructions as if they were small children at a sleepover.

"Marshall, don't you go snooping around Belle's house, you know how nosy you is," she said. "Esau Tate, make sure that you brush your teeth before you go to bed."

This would be the first time that the Tate men would be able to relax without Rosalie's supervision and badgering.

Perhaps, the father and son would have an opportunity to bond with her nowhere in sight.

Joe Bamo spent his first night alone ever without Nettie at their home over on Oglethorpe Road across from the cemetery. Before leaving Nettie at Elenora's house, the two of them sat on the front porch just like they used to do when Fannie Mae was still alive. Finally, they reluctantly said, "Goodnight."

Royce, Horace Lee, Bobby Lee and Cleophus, continued the bachelor party back at Royce's house where they would stay for the night. They did shots of Moonshine with beer chasers. They gave Bobby Lee the responsibility of getting everyone up on time. Horace Lee's father, Sam, promised to call each of their cell phones the next morning.

Priscilla Jenkins drove by her brother's house and saw Horace Lee's car in the driveway, but decided not to stop. Royce would not be amused by her intrusion or her desperate attempt to see the groom on the night before his wedding. She was not invited to the wedding the next day for obvious reasons. She could not risk being a wedding crasher and face the ire of Marshall Tate again.

CHAPTER 17

THERE IS ALWAYS A MORNING AFTER (LET US REJOICE AND BE FREE)

The smell of slab bacon wafted through the house, signaling that Belle was in the kitchen. Fannie Mae's girls were so excited about Christine's wedding day that they could hardly sleep the night before. They sat up until about 2:00 a.m., talking about how beautiful the wedding would be and how they wished that Fannie Mae and Henry Turner could be there to see their daughter get married — especially Fannie Mae, since she always expressed her dislike for the fact that, "Christine and Horace Lee were living in sin up there in Atlanta."

Fannie Mae would be so proud. Somehow they knew that Fannie Mae's spirit would be hovering over the ceremony at New Ebenezer First Missionary Baptist Church. She would be giving her blessing in absentia. She and God would be smiling down upon the Turner and Miller families as Christine and Horace Lee were joined in holy matrimony.

Belle's breakfast cooking was like an alarm clock to their senses. One by one, they came into the kitchen to join their oldest sister. It felt like Fannie Mae had been reincarnated. Esau, Marshall and Joe Bamo joined the sleep-deprived Turner sisters for breakfast. The three of them arrived just in time to see the Turner sisters still in their nightgowns with hairnets to hold their hairstyles in place until Jerome or Neesha showed up to put the final touches on them after Elenora completed the bridal party's makeup. Marshall was willing to bet that Jerome's alter ego Neesha would be showing up on the day of the wedding, not only as the bridal party hairstylist, but as a guest as well. Rosalie hoped that her son's drag-queen friend would not draw attention away from the bride on her wedding day. Marshall was already enough to attract attention to start tongues wagging.

On the other hand, the men over at Royce Jenkins, house in Ellaville had a difficult time just opening their eyes. They were all hungover from too much booze. The order of the day was a big pot of coffee and an assortment of hangover remedies. Any smell of food cooking would only make them sicker. They all felt like they had pulled an all-nighter at the Magic City strip club up in Atlanta. Horace Lee had always wanted his bachelor party to be held at Magic City; however, it would have been logistically impossible to have a bachelor party more than 100-miles away, given the fact that all of the groomsmen lived in South Georgia. Horace Lee promised the guys that he would host them at Magic City in Atlanta at some point in the future; but for now, they settled for an old-fashioned, country-style blowout right in the church parking lot and at Royce Jenkins' house. Joe Bamo, Esau and Sam Miller took the right approach and left the church with their wives. They were not hungover on the wedding day.

Sam Miller started calling the cell phones of Royce, Cleophus, Bobby Lee and Horace Lee at around 9:00 a.m., to no avail. All of the calls went straight to voicemail. After trying for about a half hour, he decided to drive over to Royce's house to rally the troops. He knocked at the front door first, then the side window, and then finally at the rear of the house. The four men were all passed out on the living-room floor. Royce finally opened the back door and looked like hell. Sam Miller could only wonder what the others looked like. He imagined that they would all have to wear sunglasses during the wedding ceremony to hide their bloodshot eyes. When Sam entered Royce's kitchen, he could hear his two sons and Cleophus scrambling to straighten up. Sam Miller could smell the stench of cigar smoke mixed with stale beer and corn whiskey.

"Good morning, Mr. Miller," Cleophus muttered with his head held low.

"Hey, Daddy," Bobby Lee said under his breath.

Horace Lee just held his head in both hands in shame.

Sam Miller laughed and said, "You are a sorry bunch of no-count drunks. Get yourselves cleaned up and come on over to the house so that we can sober you fools up before the wedding," he ordered Horace Lee and his groomsmen.

Back at Elenora's, the Turner sisters were all bathed and ready for their wedding makeup session. Elenora applied her own makeup first. Then she applied the makeup for Belle, Nettie and

Rosalie. She saved Christine for last. She wanted the bride-to-be to look like absolute perfection and to be picture perfect.

Neesha arrived at Elenora's house with her hairstyling assistant Wendy in tow. Marshall greeted his two drag queen friends from Albany with air kisses.

"Don't mess my makeup up, Miss Thing!" hollered Neesha.

"Your face is really beaten something fierce!" declared Marshall as he did his signature three finger snaps in the air in big circles.

The three friends just knew that they would wreck the wedding of Christine and Horace Lee. Only the bride would be fiercer than the girls from Albany, Georgia. Neesha was dressed in a two-piece suit with a Mandarin collar and gold braided closures in Chinese red Shantung silk. Her wig was styled in Geisha-girl fashion and adorned on each side with a golden hair comb. She wore red-silk, backless pumps with three-inch heels in size 11 and carried a matching handbag with gold metallic accents. Neesha also wore dangling gold chandelier earrings and matching bangle bracelets. Wendy, on the other hand, went for the Marilyn Monroe Hollywood ingénue look. She wore a designer replica of the famous white dress that Marilyn Monroe wore in the film "The Seven Year Itch." Her version was done in a bright cherry red with the same halter-top and full pleated skirt for the windblown look. Her platinum blonde hair and makeup were styled after her movie idol, and she wore a pair of silver naked high heels with ankle straps. Wendy accessorized her glamour look with sterling-silver earrings and bracelet with red semi-precious stones. Neesha wore a silver fox jacket, and Wendy topped her ensemble with a full-length white mink coat. They, along with Marshall in his winter-white suit and red accessories, would turn New Ebenezer First Missionary Baptist Church upside down and inside out. They would have to constantly remind themselves that they were not the brides today.

When Marshall escorted Neesha and Wendy into the house, Miss Fannie Mae's girls were waiting for their hair to be touched up for the wedding. They had vaguely remembered Marshall's friends from their mother's wake at Meadows Oglethorpe Funeral Chapel. What they did not remember was just how over the top they were. Poor Nettie in her own little, quiet way showed a total delight and amusement by these two man-sized women in her midst. She felt completely overpowered by the bigger-than-life personas of Neesha and Wendy. Rosalie was accustomed to the two of them in and out of drag. She knew Neesha when she was just plain, old Jerome with buckteeth and nappy hair, and Wendy as a skinny and scraggly Wendell. They both attended high school with Marshall — and like him, they were treated as outcasts by most of the student body. The trio of teens was ostracized and bullied by many of the boys. They refused to take gym class for fear of being roughed up by their classmates. Many of the girls accepted them and were empathetic to their plight. The three boys formed their own little social club and proudly embraced their sexuality. When it was time for the senior prom, they attended with three girls who were lesbians-in-training. Marshall, Jerome and Wendell remained best friends ever since.

Elenora and Christine, who respectively lived in New York

and Atlanta, were not at all shocked by the appearance of the faux women from Albany. They welcomed them into Miss Fannie Mae's house — and the wedding-day gabfest was on.

"Ooh child, we is got some work to be done up in here!" Neesha said to Elenora. "Y'all got any beer? I need me a drink!"

Rosalie had grabbed a six-pack of beer from Bobby Lee's trunk the night before. "I got my own private stash in the fridge, here you go, Sugar." She also handed a beer to Wendy and said, "Honey, you look like you can use one too!"

"Thanks, ma'am," Wendy said to Rosalie.

Marshall, Christine and Elenora fell silent with raised eyebrows just waiting for what would come next.

"Who you calling ma'am?" exclaimed Rosalie. "I ain't your mama! You better put your joke book up!" scolded Rosalie without breaking a smile.

Then she hugged Wendy affectionately as she used to when he was known as Wendell.

"Thank you, Mrs. Tate, oh hell, I mean Miss Rosalie."

"Don't worry, you can just call me Big Red!" replied Rosalie.

Wendy felt very comforted being held by Rosalie. She was always the only parent that Wendell and Jerome could talk to whenever they were feeling like outcasts, just like her own son, Marshall.

Neesha and Wendy donned smocks over their fine wedding clothes and set about styling the hair of the Turner sisters, taking special care with Christine.

"You are going to be as beautiful and fierce as we are," said Neesha.

Christine did not know whether to feel good about the comment or to cry her eyes out. Elenora let out a big "whoop" and rolled her eyes very dramatically in the direction of Nettie and away from Neesha and Wendy.

Nettie, in an effort to not be excluded from the conversation, decided to put her two cents in by saying, "I think you both are beautiful women, but what does 'fierce mean?'"

All of the other women just giggled and let it be. But, Marshall could not resist. "Aunt Nettie, this here is fierce!" he said as he posed and moved his hands up and down his body. Nettie quickly got the message.

The white-and-burgundy silk orchid hairclips were affixed to the hairstyles of Belle, Nettie, Rosalie and Elenora. Christine's hair was styled in a Jackie "O" style chic hairdo. The classic bob was smooth and elegant to properly support her pillbox hat and veil. She had been transformed from an average-looking country girl into a sleek-and-sophisticated woman. The only problem was her gold teeth that were hard not to notice. She was not ashamed of them, but decided that she would soon get rid of the gold in her mouth.

This was her day, and no one was going to upstage Christine "Sweetie Pie" Turner.

Back during the 1960s, Fannie Mae Turner always had pictures around the house of President John F. Kennedy and his wife, Jacqueline; his brother Robert Kennedy and his wife, Ethel; Medgar Evers and his wife, Myrlie; and, of course, the Reverend Dr. Martin Luther King, Jr. and his wife, Coretta. She often reminded her girls that they needed to be strong and independent women. She always used these four widows of slain martyrs during the civil rights era as examples of women who had survived adversity and hardship. They reminded her of her own mother and how she was able to carry on after her husband, Buck Jessup, mysteriously disappeared in 1927. Jesse Jessup never let Fannie Mae know how difficult life was without a man around the house. She never ever let Fannie Mae see her cry. She suffered in silence and privacy much like many other women of her time did when their men disappeared without a trace. Their years were filled with anxiety, as they tried to raise male children with dignity and purpose in the Deep South. Things were no different in Oglethorpe, Georgia than they were in Selma, Alabama. It took the bloody beatings, mutilations and deaths of many black men as well as the assassinations of John, Medgar, Martin, and Bobby before things began to change throughout the "Land of the Free." Despite his assassination in 1963, John F. Kennedy's efforts resulted in the Civil Rights Act signed into law in 1964. Fannie Mae Turner then began to have hope for the future of her five daughters and future generations to come.

CHAPTER 18

GET READY (CAUSE HERE WE COME)

"You boys look like you could use a real home-cooked breakfast this morning to help get rid of whatever ails you," Horace Lee's mother said to the young men seated at her kitchen table.

"What on Earth did y'all get into last night after the wedding rehearsal?" asked her husband.

"Nothing much to talk about, Mr. Miller," replied Royce.

Sam Miller shook his head knowing very well that judging by the motley crew he saw before him, there was nothing more further from the truth.

"You wouldn't lie to me now, would you, son?" he asked of no one in particular, but they all lowered their heads at the same time, which told it all.

"Daddy, we just had a quiet night and went to sleep early,"

Bobby Lee finally answered through bloodshot eyes, almost forgetting that his father had just found them earlier strewn all over the floor at Royce's house.

"Well my wife's cooking is a sure cure for almost everything that ails you including young men who tell lies," said Sam.

The faces of the guilty and the accused could not hide the truth any longer.

Sam Miller just smiled at Horace Lee and said, "Son, last night was your night. I'm just glad that you all spent the night at Royce's and not way up the road in Atlanta. No telling if y'all ever would've made it back for the wedding."

Hortense Miller fixed Horace Lee, Bobby Lee, Cleophus and Royce a hardy breakfast of thick-sliced salt pork and fat back, cheese grits, scrambled eggs, biscuits and strong coffee.

"Now you boys eat up every bit of this here food that I done fixed for y'all," said Hortense. "I don't want no scraps left for them mangy dogs outside."

Sam Miller made each of them drink his hangover remedy to settle their stomachs and to sooth their achy heads. It was a concoction of tomato juice with raw egg and Tabasco sauce.

"Drink up every drop," he told them.

It tasted horrible, but they sobered up quickly.

Mr. and Mrs. Miller told the four young men to just relax themselves in order to get over the jitters that normally accompanied a bad hangover. It was important that they be able to conduct themselves properly during the wedding, especially the groom.

"You've got just three hours before you have to be at the church at 2:00 p.m.," Hortense told them.

The wedding was scheduled to take place at 3:00 p.m. sharp!

As Marshall Tate had told everyone the night before, "This don't mean black people's time. This don't mean colored folk's time. I mean white folk's time!"

The guests would start arriving at about 2:15 p.m. Horace Lee would have to spend some time with Pastor Hicks before the ceremony started, and the groomsmen would have to seat the guests after they were greeted by Carrie Lee Miller. Joe Bamo was scheduled to meet them at the church. He would definitely be on time, because he would be the only one of the five men in the wedding party without a slight hangover.

The limousine that Esau hired from a company in Americus, Georgia was scheduled to arrive at Elenora's house to pick up Christine and her sisters at 2:30 p.m. Marshall would make sure that they were all dressed and ready to go.

"I don't want no foolishness out of none of y'all," he warned them.

Esau, Marshall, Neesha and Wendy would follow the limo in Neesha's 1999 white Cadillac Sedan de Ville. Esau Tate had also known Marshall's friends Jerome and Wendell since they were in high school with his son. He also knew them just as much as Neesha and Wendy. He was extremely comfortable in their presence. On the other hand, his brother-in-law Joe Bamo was as skittish around them as a cat with a tail in a room full of rocking chairs. He did not know by what name to refer to them. Should he say him or her, ma'am or sir, mister or miss? When he stopped by Elenora's house to see Nettie before getting ready for the wedding, he did not know what to make of the two new women who were styling the hair of the bride and bridesmaids. Joe Bamo did a double take at the ladies in red. He looked them up and down from head to toe. Standing before him, they were dead ringers for Marilyn Monroe and a black-Chinese madam, both with hands and feet bigger than his.

He could not stop staring until he heard Marshall's voice, "Neesha and Wendy, this is my Uncle Joe Bamo, the quiet one."

Joe Bamo tried to withdraw when the two Amazon women tried to squeeze him in between them. He ended up with bright red lipstick on both cheeks. Needless to say, he beat a hasty retreat back to his car. He almost forgot to say "hello" to his wife, Nettie. The other Turner sisters got a real kick out of their brother-in-law running like a scared cat from Neesha and Wendy.

"Ooh child, I never seen Joe Bamo move so fast in my life!" Rosalie cried out.

These two "women" from Albany, Georgia had a similar affect on most men they met, especially those who were unaware of their true identity.

Neesha and Wendy helped the maid of honor and each of the bridesmaids into their beautiful Bordeaux Midnight Red dresses so that they would not disturb the hairdos that they worked so hard to create. They each wore matching ruby-red crystal teardrop earrings and the satin pumps that were dyed to match the dresses. The last to get dressed was the bride Christine. Her eldest sister Belle, who had so lovingly made her wedding ensemble, and her younger sister, the maid of honor Elenora, helped her to get dressed. Elenora loaned her a sterling-silver, white cubic zirconia tennis bracelet for the something borrowed, and Belle pinned Fannie Mae's powder-blue lace handkerchief into the inside of her jacket for good luck and for something blue. Christine looked like a fairy-tale snow princess in her Candlelight White Duchesse Peau de Soie dress with matching Ming Brocade jacket. Her wedding ensemble was topped off with the white Jackie "O" pillbox hat with the short veil that Belle had made and a pair of button pearl earrings. The bridal and bridesmaids bouquets sat in a large, white basket by the door so that Marshall would not forget them.

The white stretch limousine arrived from Americus at least a half-hour early. The driver knew from past experience that bridal parties were seldom ready on time. What he did not know was that Marshall Tate, wedding-planner extraordinaire, was in charge. Marshall had the bridal party dressed, ready and inside, waiting for their limo when it arrived. He intended for them to arrive at the church in plenty of time before the start of the ceremony at 3:00 p.m., just after the last guests had entered the church and been seated. Marshall and the bridal party entered the church and assembled in a private room just to the left of the main entrance hall.

Elenora took a seat right away after they entered the room, and then she heard Marshall scold her, "Stand, don't sit! I don't want one single wrinkle on not one dress!"

After that, no one else dared to make an attempt to sit.

"Excuse me!" Elenora shot back as she stood to his command.

Sam Miller drove Horace Lee, Bobby Lee, Cleophus and Royce from Ellaville to New Ebenezer First Missionary Baptist Church over in Oglethorpe in Royce Jenkins' Cadillac Escalade. The Escalade, with its large expensive rims, was a bit ostentatious for Ellaville, Georgia. His neighbors always suspected that Royce was involved in something nefarious, but had no proof of criminal activity. Carrie Lee and Hortense Miller followed the men in a separate car. Joe Bamo arrived to meet the groom's party at the church at the exact same time, 2:00 p.m.

Horace Lee joined Pastor Hicks in the pastor's study. Bobby Lee Miller, Royce Jenkins, Cleophus Jones and Joe Bamo positioned themselves at the church sanctuary doors. Carrie Lee Miller was stationed at the podium in the church entry hall that held the guest book. The same red-and-white ribbons and bow that decorated the pews reserved for the family festooned the podium. Hortense Miller, the mother of the groom, waited in a small alcove to the right of the entry hall.

Pastor Hicks greeted Horace Lee and noticed right away that the groom acted nervous and jittery. "You all right, son?" he asked the groom.

At first, he thought that his fidgety agitation was directly related to the last-minute jitters and butterflies that most grooms experience on their wedding day. Upon closer inspection, he realized that Horace Lee's impromptu bachelor party probably had gone on too long. The number of groomsmen wearing sunglasses inside the church should have been his first clue.

"Are you sure that you are ready to carry on with this today?" Pastor Hicks asked.

"I guess so," replied Horace Lee.

"This is no time for guessing; you have to be more certain than that," continued Pastor Hicks.

"I mean 'yes,' I am sure," responded Horace Lee.

Pastor Hicks reminded him that there would be a place during the ceremony where he would relinquish control to the bride and groom to recite their personal vows to one another. "Are you prepared for that?"

Horace Lee nodded slowly with his head bowed.

"Just relax and the Lord will see you through," advised the Pastor as his final words.

Horace Lee sat quietly while Pastor Hicks studied the scriptures for the wedding ceremony.

The Johnson twins, Purvis and Percival, had lined the front steps of New Ebenezer First Missionary Baptist Church with red-and-white potted flowers. They had tied large red bows with red-and-white streaming ribbons to the railings. Once again, they had followed Marshall Tate's instructions to the letter. They knew that he would be pleased with their handiwork.

The guests started to arrive on time. There were those who wanted to get to the church early so that they could get an up-front seat. They wanted to be up close and personal to Horace Lee and Christine. The nearer that they sat to the altar, the better it would be to see and hear everything. Carol Neptune and her young boyfriend were among the first to arrive. Carol wanted to make sure that every guest who entered the church could see her and her new beau picked fresh from the cradle. She wore the shortest red dress that she could find. It was nearly impossible for her to sit down without giving a full view of her red-lace panties. She might as well have worn a scarlet letter on her forehead to signify that she and she alone was the town floozy. Edna Green and Dottie Fields arrived together. Edna had on a huge, floppy red-felt hat and a red-and-white polka-dot dress that she had forgot to iron.

Dottie had dyed her coarse Brillo-pad Afro a two-toned bright red-and-yellowish blonde. There were stains around her temples and forehead from the red hair dye. Here it was the middle of February, and she was wearing a bright red-and-yellow striped sundress about the same color as her hair. With her light complexion and pancake makeup, Dottie Fields looked like Ronald McDonald's twin sister.

It would not be important as to who the guests were or what they were wearing, except for the mere fact that many of them were a great deal more interesting than the bride and groom. Some of the guests simply came to see what others would be wearing given the Valentine's Day theme that Marshall Tate had set forth for the wedding. Marshall, known for his excesses, had also leaked the guest list to the local press as if the wedding of Horace Lee Miller and Christine Turner was somehow on the same level as Prince Charles and Lady Diana. The reporter, who usually reported on births, deaths, weddings and funerals, and the goings on with the local 4-H Club, would be covering the Turner-Miller nuptials.

The rural city of Oglethorpe in Macon County, tucked away out in the middle of nowhere, on the banks of the Flint River in South Georgia, was by no means known for its fashion sense. Different from the out-of-towners, who would certainly be turned out in the latest styles, the locals were sure not to disappoint in their outrageous fashions.

Most of the guests adhered to the red-color theme in honor of Valentine's Day, but some went entirely overboard. Jefferson Davis Williams and his wife, Beulah, wore matching outfits with hearts all over them. He wore a red-velvet jacket with satin hearts stitched around the cuffs, and she had on a red-velvet empire dress with satin hearts around the waist and hem. Beulah Williams made the clothing for herself and her husband. They were always the talk of the town every Sunday after church.

On the other hand, his cousin Wayne Williams, an attorney with Thomas Allen's law firm, wore a charcoal gray Hugo Boss suit with a tone-on-tone, red-and-white thin pinstripe shirt from Polo by Ralph Lauren and a Bill Blass tie with finite, almost invisible red pin dots. On his feet, he wore a pair of dark burgundy Eduardo G shoes that were handmade in Portugal. His only accessories were his signature vintage Breitling watch and a chain-link bracelet with an anchor-locking clasp. It is important to note his attire because in addition to being a fashion oddity in Oglethorpe, Wayne Williams was the best-dressed and most eligible bachelor in all of South Georgia. He dressed like the big-city lawyers up in Atlanta. Wayne was born and raised up north in Philadelphia with Georgia family roots. He had attended Howard University School of Law in Washington, D.C. with Thomas Allen and decided to relocate to Macon County to join his friend's law practice. Clients came from all over South Georgia to the Allen Law Firm just to have either of these two very accomplished attorneys handle their cases and legal business. Fannie Mae Turner trusted them completely to handle her affairs. The two men sat in the same pew along with Thomas Allen's wife, Patricia, their legal secretary, Helen Mills, Steven James, Robin Hammond and Melvin Cason. Melvin Cason was Pastor Hicks' most dedicated, loyal and trusted church executive. Without him, New Ebenezer First Missionary Baptist Church would neither operate nor function. They were a close-knit, church-going family thanks to the devoted leadership of Mr. Cason.

The rest of the wedding guests included distant family members and friends on both sides. They came from various parts of Georgia and from around the country. There were the four Storey sisters and their husbands. Lillian, Dianne, Doris and Gwen Storey grew up with the Turner sisters in South Georgia. Ethel Young, Helen Prysock, Edna Thompson, her ex-husband George and his new wife Loretta; John Eddings and his wife, Carole; Mattie Walton, Sandra Mabry, John Henry Johnson; Delores Bell and her daughter Dara Francis; Dale and Edna Kessler; Roger and Rose Duckett; Christine Lewis and her son Bobby Dixon; Jeffrey and Darlene McCoy; Virginia Banks; and a host of others were all there to share in the happiest day for Horace Lee Miller and Christine Turner.

Because this was truly a major social event for small town Oglethorpe, Georgia with guests from so far away, the local Macon County newspaper reporter made sure to take special note of all who were in attendance and what they were wearing. This wedding was the most exciting event to happen in a long time in this part of the state.

Even John Henry Johnson's cousin Mamie Talmadge came all the way from Philadelphia for the wedding. She had become friends with Fannie Mae and the Turner sisters over many years of visiting South Georgia. Like Ethel Hicks' sister, Doris Sherard from Atlanta, Mamie was a very busy socialite who played bridge frequently and traveled extensively around the world, but she always found time to travel back home to Georgia.

Also sitting on the bride's side was the Turner's cousin Richard Wood and his beautiful wife Sarah, affectionately known as Pinkie, also from Atlanta. Ricky and Pinkie often included Christine and Horace Lee as their holiday dinner guests. Ricky Wood was famously known around Atlanta for his cooking and culinary skills, especially his barbecue ribs. He had packed a cooler full of his famous ribs in the trunk of his car for the newlyweds to enjoy.

Another intriguing and very interesting guest was Lili Santa Maria Pfeiffer, a beautiful-and-elegant, Uruguayan-born woman who befriended Elenora Turner while she lived in New York City. Lili had introduced Elenora to the line of cosmetics that she used to do the makeup for the bridal party. The two had become close friends, often having lunch together in Central Park. She was one of the few people besides Fannie Mae who really understood Lena Turner. Lili understood that Elenora was a troubled soul who needed a mature mother figure in her life since she was so far away from her family and all alone. She also felt like she knew Fannie Mae and Elenora's sisters very well. She was honored to accept the invitation to Christine and Horace Lee's wedding. Lili looked like a Spanish queen in her red-satin dress with its high-collar, matching cashmere Pashmina and faux fur hand-warmer muff. She was too politically correct and concerned about the plight of animals to wear real fur. Nonetheless, her look was regal and royal. Lili had nailed the look of Spanish royalty! She was also partly responsible for Elenora's sense of style.

Shirley Floyd strolled into the sanctuary looking like Diana Ross. She wore a ruby-red couture suit with white stitching and a heart-shaped neckline from chic-and-trendy Paris designer Adrienne DuPlesse along with a matching, large-brimmed floppy hat. Like Ethel Hicks, Shirley Floyd liked her one-of-a-kind designer clothes. Shirley sat with her three sisters-in-law, Ethel Young, Helen Prysock and Edna Thompson, who were also turned out in high-fashion red. They were one of the two fashion power pews in the church for the Turner-Miller wedding; the other fashion power pew was occupied by Jean Cunningham, Jackie Fraser, Jacqueline Epps, and Judy Anderson and her husband, Ralph, along with Carolyn Adams, Greg Pratt and Yvonne Manning. When this group of femme-fatales and dashing men from Richmond, Virginia entered the sanctuary of New Ebenezer First Missionary Baptist Church, all heads turned and all chatter came to a halt. A silence bathed the room. This didn't faze them at all — they were used to stopping traffic wherever they went. Today was no exception.

Ethel Hicks' sister and society-maven Doris Sherard came down from Atlanta for the wedding. She drove down with her daughter Delores, her son-in-law Nelson, and their daughter Deborah. Doris' nephew Daniel Ware, who was Fannie Mae's personal banker, joined them at the church. Behind them sat

Ronald Gay, Laura Stevens, Bernie Spraggins, Samuel Wallace and his wife, Janice.

If there were prizes for the most outlandish and overdone outfits, they would have gone to Ronald Gibson of Americus, Jefferson Davis and Beulah Williams, and to Neesha and Wendy from Albany. Ronald Gibson wore a three-piece red suit, red shirt, red tie, red derby hat, red shoes and red socks — and he topped it off with a white cashmere double-breasted, maxi-length coat. No one stood out more than Ronald, the Williamses and the two ladies in red-with-white mink and silver fox furs — all in that order. Carol Neptune, her short skirt and her younger-than-young boyfriend soon became yesterday's news when those three walked into the church.

While the guests were being greeted and seated at New Ebenezer First Missionary Baptist Church in Oglethorpe, there was a flurry of activity over at the Meade-Brown Mansion in Montezuma where the reception was to be held. Tom Meade III, Robert Steven Brown and their staff were putting the final touches on the grand hall. Tom and Robert had been partners in love for more than 20 years and had refurbished and restored Tom's grandfather's old home to its former stately elegance and glory. The mansion had hosted many social events throughout the years, but weddings and wedding receptions were always their favorites. Tom and Robert always dreamed of having their own wedding at Meade-Brown Mansion ever since they attended the wedding of their close friends Mark Duncan and Steve Dearlove in Toronto, Canada in the spring of 2006. They knew that there would be a cold day in hell before the state of Georgia would ever pass a law giving same-sex couples the right to legally marry. If they were married in another state or country where it was legal, they still would not be recognized as being legally married in Macon County, Georgia. For now, they would settle for just being Meade-Brown in name only.

At the head table, they placed name cards for the wedding party along with the bridesmaids' and groomsmen's gifts. They placed the bridesmaids' sterling-silver, heart-shaped measuring spoon sets in red-velvet boxes tied with white-silk organza ribbons. For each of the groomsmen, Horace Lee had selected a gift of a stainless-steel hip flask engraved with each of their names and wrapped each in red-velvet drawstring pouches. They placed burgundy-and-white orchid centerpieces in glass vases surrounded by votive candles, waiting to be lit on the head table and tables where the guests would be seated using the table number according to the seating chart.

The table-seating chart, also prepared by Marshall Tate for the reception guests, was to be followed to the letter with no exceptions. He instructed the catering director, Beverly Alexander, not to accept any requests from the guests to change seats. He knew that some of the more tacky invitees would try to muscle their way to another table where a friend or relative was seated. Marshall vowed that anyone who was caught moving to another table would first be embarrassed and humiliated publicly by him and then personally escorted from the reception hall. He had a reputation for his brash straightforward manner and was not to be crossed.

"I will not suffer fools," he told Ms. Alexander.

She had her staff on "red alert" to be on the lookout for anyone that violated Marshall Tate's rules of etiquette. She did not want Marshall to cause a scene in the historic Meade-Brown pre-Civil War mansion in Montezuma, Georgia. The South would surely rise up again. The former Klansmen, Tom Meade, Robert Brown and Mack Murray, were already starting a slow turn in their graves.

Deloris Ellison had decorated the two cake tables with red rose petals and red crystal beads. On the larger table, she placed the three-tiered, heart-shaped white wedding cake with red piping. Instead of the traditional bride-and-groom cake topper, Deloris custom designed a cake topper of two interlocking red hearts made out of spun sugar. She was pure genius when it came to creating the best wedding cakes in all of South Georgia. She decorated the table holding the groom's red-velvet cake, a red, white and black replica of Atlanta Falcons' former quarterback Michael Vick's #7 jersey, with red, white and black football-shaped jelly beans. Horace Lee would be both surprised and pleased that he was honored with this special Falcons' fan cake.

The DJ, Cool Curtis Mo D from Ideal, Georgia had his equipment all set up and ready to go for when the bride and groom and their guests arrived at Meade-Brown Mansion. He also had a playlist of selections requested by Marshall Tate and his own selections for continuous dance music for a four-hour reception.

The head chef had hired extra cooks from the local African-American community around Montezuma to help in the preparation of Fannie Mae Turner's Sunday Supper menu for the wedding reception. He did not want Marshall Tate marching into his kitchen all fired up and throwing a hissy fit. The food had to be just as if Fannie Mae had prepared it herself. There was no room for error. It was just that matter of fact and to the point. The wedding reception for Mr. and Mrs. Horace Lee Miller would be just as their wedding planner had designed it.

CHAPTER 19

JUMPING THE BROOM (AT LAST)

Rebecca Murray Pope and her assistant photographer Joe Lackey were positioned on either side of the altar. She had earlier photographed Christine and her sisters before they left home for the church, then again after they arrived at the church, and also in the private room just off of the main entrance hall. Rebecca wanted to capture the Turner sisters in personal moments in a more natural setting. She wanted to photograph them in their comfort zone and in their own environment. What she had not bargained for were the two "extra" women from Albany, Georgia, Wendy and Neesha. Rebecca was particularly careful to keep them out of the viewfinder and out of focus whenever she was shooting the real women in the wedding party. Despite her efforts to try and keep them out of the photos, they kept finding ways to insert themselves in them.

When Rebecca Murray Pope had enough of their antics and posing for the camera, she finally said to no one in particular, "If you ain't in this wedding, then stay out of the way!"

Neesha was the first to speak up, "Now wait a minute Miss Lady with a camera! Who the hell you think you talkin' to?"

Then Wendy chimed in, "Oh no she didn't!"

Marshall Tate stepped in between and on the side of the photographer to diffuse the situation, "If you ain't paying Rebecca Murray Pope by the hour to take these damn pictures, then you better stay the hell out of her way!"

That ended it right there. The other two sat down quietly without another sound.

During the wedding, Rebecca would be photographing the bridesmaids, maid of honor and the bride as they walked down the aisle while Joe would capture the wedding action in and around the altar and throughout the sanctuary. Both would shoot the actual wedding ceremony from various angles and visual perspectives. For assurance, Marshall asked Steve James, who was an invited guest and a professional photographer from Philadelphia, to bring his equipment just in case something was missed.

In his usual manner, Marshall did not ask, instead he simply told Steve, "Don't you dare bother showing up down here in Oglethorpe, Georgia without your camera equipment packed in your suitcase!"

Steve replied, "How much are you paying and when?"

Marshall's wicked tongue with a coating of sugar shot back in an instant response, "How's about a great big kiss as soon as you get here?"

That was enough for Steve to agree to just about anything, just to end the conversation. Steve was requested to discreetly capture the wedding and the reception from his own personal perspective without interfering with Rebecca and Joe.

"Now don't you go getting in nobody else's way but mine, you hear me, Sugar?" were his instructions from Marshall.

Steve got the message and planned to stay out of everyone's way while taking pictures, especially one Marshall Tate.

The altar was adorned with the floral arrangements created by the designer at Michael's in Warner Robins, Georgia. He had taken the liberty of adding long-stemmed amaryllis flowers in red and white to the original design of burgundy-and-white roses. This made the silk flower arrangements even grander and sure to please. Marshall Tate was very impressed by how Ethel Hicks carried out the task of ordering the bridal bouquets and floral arrangements for the wedding and the reception. He was even more impressed by the floral designer at Michael's and assumed that he was gay as well, considering how elegant the arrangements were. Marshall hated stereotyping another man based upon his occupation, but he was curious all the same. He made a mental note to stop by and introduce himself to him the next time that he was in Warner Robins or Macon. With that kind of floral design talent, perhaps they could do business together in the future. Or, just do business together period!

Marshall Tate would probably ask him in his usual high-pitched sing-song voice, "Don't want to do nothing, do you?" or, "How about a little something, something?"

Those were the pickup lines that he used mostly on unsuspecting men around the center of town in Albany. He was usually more lucky than not. Sometimes he got more than he bargained for. Once he even got jail time for soliciting an undercover vice officer.

The first pews of the Sanctuary reserved for immediate family on either side of the aisle each had a large red bow and red-and-white streaming ribbons that Purvis and Percival had placed the day before. Their handiwork had passed inspection and had received approval from the almighty wedding planner Marshall Tate.

Bobby Lee Miller escorted his mother, Hortense, followed by his father, Sam, to their reserved pew. Carrie Lee Miller sat in the pew behind her parents after she had greeted the last guests to arrive. Next to her sat their cousin Walter Miller and his beautiful wife, Shirley, from Richmond, Virginia; their other cousin Alvin Watford and his lovely wife, Marva, from Westchester County, New York; and Hortense Miller's sister Maybelline Crocker and her husband, Jasper, from Buena Vista, Georgia.

Joe Bamo carefully placed Fannie Mae Turner's light-blue satin pillow trimmed in white lace with her name embroidered on it in the seat that was reserved for the mother of the bride. He then escorted Ethel Hicks to her seat of honor beside Fannie Mae's pillow. All of the guests were seated and chatted with those nearby as well as from pew to pew. They were the new family and friends meeting the old. There were those who had not seen one another for a while or since the last funeral or wedding. Old acquaintances were renewed. And of course, there was the obligatory gossip that always takes place at weddings and funerals — this was no exception.

A hush came over the church as the door to the Pastor's study opened. Out walked Pastor Hicks followed by Horace Lee Miller. With his new haircut, Horace Lee was tall, dark and extremely handsome. He resembled the black-English actor Idris Elba of "American Gangster" fame and the film "Obsessed" with Beyonce Knowles. He was dark chocolate and very sexy. Horace Lee filled out his tuxedo as if he was poured into it. The silence was broken by a series of "oohs" and "aahs" from some of the women in the church as he stood next to Pastor Hicks facing the wedding guests. Christine had made herself quite a catch.

Carol Neptune could be heard above the other voices saying, "I bet that Priscilla Jenkins over in Ellaville is about to slit her wrists, I know I would."

Her comment brought laughter from those around her.

There was only one other man in the church who matched the groom in overall handsomeness, good looks and sexuality — and that was Wayne Williams from the Allen Law Firm. Thomas Allen and John Henry Johnson were considered pretty boys around Macon County, but Horace Lee Miller and Wayne Williams were ruggedly handsome — just what women wanted.

Bobby Lee Miller, Royce Jenkins, Cleophus Jones and Joe Bamo joined Pastor Hicks and Horace Lee at the front of the church. All of the men stood with their bodies angled and facing toward the pews and the rear of the church from where the bridesmaids, maid of honor, and finally the bride escorted by Esau Tate would walk down the aisle.

On cue from Marshall Tate, Bertha Hightower started the intro music to Jeffrey Osborne's "On the Wings of Love," followed by Anita Robinson's singing. The center doors at the rear of the church opened and there stood Belle, the eldest of Miss Fannie Mae's girls. The wedding guests turned slightly in their pews to get a good look. They did not want to miss one step of the wedding processional. As Anita hit the first note, Belle started down the aisle. There were audible gasps of delight at the sight of the sheer beauty of the bridesmaid's dress that she not only wore but had made as well. The dress was atypical of most bridesmaid dresses that are absolutely despised by those who have to wear them. The stylish Bordeaux Midnight Red dress was rich and elegant.

Nettie, then Rosalie and finally Elenora followed Belle. Each of them was evenly spaced apart and in complete rhythmic syncopation with the musical talents of Bertha Hightower and Anita Robinson. They each put on their own signature walk as they headed down the aisle, carrying their bouquets of deep red camellias with one white camellia in the center and wearing beautiful white-and-burgundy orchid hair clips in their hair. They totally ignored Marshall's instructions on how the walk should be done. After all, they were his elders and as the old folks used to say to young folks in the South, "Come here can't tell been here!" He just smiled with pride as he watched his mother and aunts strut their stuff down the aisle of New Ebenezer First Missionary Baptist Church. When it was Elenora's turn, she gave the gathering just what they came to see besides the bride and groom. Her maid of honor dress had been modified to suit her taste for all things vintage 1960s. The waist was cinched and the skirt was tapered. She walked down the aisle of New Ebenezer First Missionary Baptist Church just as if she was walking the red carpet on Broadway for opening night. While walking she held her head high, looked straight ahead, and thought to herself, "You bitches better get used to it, Elenora 'Girlie' Turner is back in town."

Marshall closed the doors after Elenora started her walk down the aisle.

When it was time for the bride to walk down the aisle, Purvis and Percival Johnson rolled out the red runner and silence fell over the church until the music began again. This time Bertha Hightower and Anita Robinson launched into Roberta Flack's "The First Time Ever I Saw Your Face." The doors opened slowly and the gathering of wedding guests rose to their feet.

A broad smile crossed Horace Lee's face when he saw his bride-to-be standing in the doorway escorted by his brother-in-law-to-be, Esau Tate. He had been calm up until this point, then the butterflies in his stomach returned. His knees began to buckle and beads of sweat appeared on his forehead. Horace Lee's palms became clammy. Pastor Hicks gave him a reassuring glance and his brother, Bobby Lee, reached out to steady him. All the while he was hoping that he did not faint and fall out on the floor.

Marshall gave Esau and Christine their cue to start down the aisle. Their steps were measured and exactly perfect. When they reached the first pew at the back of the church, Christine Turner took on a glow, a confident look, and the stride of the lady who would be marrying the man who she loved so much, Horace

Lee Miller. He would be officially off the market, unavailable, and committed to her only. Christine could feel the spirit of her beloved mother, Fannie Mae, hovering above the place. She could feel the warmth of her presence. She felt guarded and protected. Nothing and no one could upset her special day, not even Priscilla Jenkins if she showed up uninvited and unannounced.

There was another audible gasp almost in unison when the wedding guests caught sight of her beautifully crafted wedding suit lovingly made by her sister Belle. The Candlelight White Ming Brocade jacket over the matching sleek Candlelight White Duchesse Peau de Soie satin dress with beaded neckline and pill-box hat with short veil were simply elegant to say the least. Her total look was breathtaking. She looked like she had just stepped right off the pages of *Modern Bride* magazine. What was even more astonishing was her "new" Jackie "O" styled hair. What was "old" can become "new" again when properly done and in good taste. Jerome "Neesha" Anderson had brought Fifth Avenue hair-styling to Macon County, Georgia. Many of the wedding guests had only known Christine to wear her hair in that outdated Jheri-curl hairdo. This was quite a transformation for Christine Turner. She looked more like a fashion mannequin rather than a local girl from the Deep South of Oglethorpe, Georgia.

To Horace Lee, Christine's walk down the aisle to join him seemed like forever and an eternity. It gave him time to steady his nerves, sturdy his knees, and to regain his balance and composure.

"Who gives this woman to this man in holy matrimony?" asked Pastor Hicks.

"I give this woman to this man in holy matrimony on behalf of the late Henry and Fannie Mae Turner," answered Esau.

He placed her hand in Horace Lee's then took his seat beside Ethel Hicks in the first pew.

Pastor Hicks continued, "Dearly beloved, we are gathered here today at New Ebenezer First Missionary Baptist Church in the presence of God and these witnesses to join Horace Lee Miller and Christine Turner together in holy matrimony. This union is deemed to be commended and honorable by all of those who are in attendance here this afternoon, therefore it is not considered by any to be ill advised or to be taken lightly, but with reverence, discretion, solid foundation, and a solemn promise. In this holy edifice, these two persons have come to be joined. If there is any person or persons who have just cause to renounce these proceedings, let them speak now or forever remain silent."

He then read the scriptures that were requested by the bride and groom. Pastor Hicks defined the holy sacrament of marriage as it pertained to the two people standing before him. He spoke of the solid family backgrounds and moral foundations from which they both came. He knew the Turner family very well, and he was beginning to know the core values of the Miller family as well. Pastor Hicks beckoned them to seize upon the heritage and opportunities that had been created before them by their respective parents and families. Most of all, he encouraged them to honor their faith in God and to love and respect one another above all others.

Horace Lee was relieved that Christine would say her personal wedding vows first. "When I first saw you, my dear Horace

Lee, when I first saw you my love, I immediately knew that I wanted to spend the rest of my life with you. When I first saw you, I immediately knew that you were the man for me. When I first saw you, I immediately knew that I wanted to love, honor and cherish you forever. When I first saw you, I hoped that you would ask me to be your wife. Now that we are standing here together on this day, I pledge myself to you forever."

Rebecca Murray Pope and Joe Lackey caught her every emotion from every angle. Everyone who knew her well felt relieved that Christine did not try to use the big fancy words that she was prone to use and completely destroy. There were no malapropisms and no faux pas. She spoke straight from her heart.

Horace Lee cleared his throat. "Christine, before I met you I thought that I would be single for the rest of my life. But after I met you, I could see myself becoming your husband even though I never told you so. Then I met your mother, and the way that she looked at me told me that I had better make up my mind and soon."

The guests who knew Fannie Mae Turner laughed at the reference to her. She was always emphatically against Christine and Horace Lee living in sin. The reference to Fannie Mae also brought about emotional feelings for her five daughters and her grandson, Marshall.

Horace Lee continued, "I wish that I had proposed to you before she died. I am sure that she would have been proud of us on this day. Fannie Mae Turner, this is for you. I will love, honor and protect your daughter Christine for as long as I live. I vow to keep her safe and free from harm forever. Thank you and God for blessing me with my lovely Christine."

There were only a few dry eyes in the church when Horace Lee finished his vows. He jokingly wiped his brow and let out a sigh of relief.

Bobby Lee Miller handed Pastor Hicks the wedding bands that he had been holding in his pocket. Pastor Hicks placed Christine's wedding band in Horace Lee's hand.

"Christine, will you accept this ring as a token of my love and devotion?"

"Yes, I will," she answered.

Then he placed Horace Lee's wedding band in Christine's hand and she asked, "Horace Lee, will you accept this ring as a symbol of my love and devotion?"

"Yes, I will," he answered.

"With the powers bestowed upon me and in the eyes of God I now pronounce you man and wife," added Pastor Hicks.

Horace Lee and Christine turned and faced the wedding guests.

"Before I present to you the new bride and groom, we have a slight change to our program," said the Pastor.

Everyone looked puzzled including the newlyweds. Marshall Tate gave Bertha Hightower the nod. She began to play one of the most recognizable songs in history and Elenora "Girlie" Turner started singing Etta James' "At Last."

"At last Horace Lee and Christine had found their dream. They had found something to cling to. At last he was hers and she was his." When Elenora finished singing the church erupted in applause with a standing ovation. Christine walked over and kissed her sister. Anita Robinson finished the musical program with her rendition of the Dolly Parton song also made famous by Whitney Houston "I Will Always Love You," to another rousing applause.

"Now I present to you Mr. and Mrs. Horace Lee Miller," said Pastor Hicks.

The entire church stood and erupted in applause again. At that moment, Ethel Hicks lay the handmade broom at their feet and the newlyweds jumped the broom on their way out of the church. Pastor Hicks and the rest of the wedding party followed them. The wedding guests remained standing until the wedding party had reached the doors of the church. The occupants of the pews followed them out in an orderly fashion as directed by Purvis and Percival Johnson.

It was the finest wedding ever to be held at New Ebenezer First Missionary Baptist Church in Oglethorpe, Georgia. For that matter, it was the finest wedding to be held in recent years in all of Macon County. It was truly a wedding to be remembered for years to come.

CHAPTER 20

WHAT'S GOING ON? (AT MEADE-BROWN MANSION)

While the new bride and groom and their wedding party were being photographed on the beautiful grounds of Meade-Brown Mansion in Montezuma, the guests who were invited to the wedding reception enjoyed cocktails and hors d'oeuvres courtesy of Fannie Mae Turner's attorneys, Thomas Allen and Wayne Williams, and her personal banker, Daniel Ware. After all, they were prominent and well-respected businessmen in the Macon County community. Also, each of them had aspirations toward a future in local politics. The reception offered the perfect opportunity to "stroke" potential voters — and fortunately for Horace Lee and Christine, to help them with the wedding reception expenses. Each bar on either side of the entrance doors to the grand hall of the mansion had a discreetly place card that read: "Sponsored by Thomas Allen and Wayne W. Williams, Allen Law Firm." And the buffet table of hors d'oeuvres had a matching place card that read: "Sponsored by Daniel D. Ware, First Mercantile Bank and Trust of Oglethorpe, Georgia."

The drink menu at both bars listed Valentine's Day themed cocktails: Pink Champagne with Strawberries, Strawberry Daiquiri, Chocolate Kiss Martini, Vodka Cranberry and Bourbon with Georgia Peach Nectar and club soda. For those who were not into frilly drinks, traditional cocktails, beer and wine were also available. The hors d'oeuvres table displayed a wide assortment of canapés, miniature crab cakes, salmon croquettes, chicken croquettes, caviar pie on toast points, spinach quiche, and chocolate and raspberry petit fours. Beverly Alexander, the catering director at Meade-Brown Mansion, was glad that the food at the cocktail reception did not go the same way as the dinner menu selected by Marshall Tate. She dreaded to think that they might be serving chitlin croquettes, collard green quiche, hush puppies, and black-eyed peas on toast points. Since Daniel Ware was paying the tab, Marshall had no say so in the matter at all. Still, she found him to be the best wedding planner and coordinator that she had ever encountered. She liked the way that he knew exactly what he wanted without exception, and with none of the second guessing that she had experienced on numerous occasions with other clients. Beverly also found him to be extremely down to earth, amusing, and downright entertaining. Most of her clients behaved like tight-assed snobs who were self-indulgent and self-impressed. In contrast, plain-old, down-to-earth Marshall Tate from Albany, Georgia spoke whatever was on his mind with a very pronounced and raucous gay lisp and made no apologies whatsoever.

The breathtaking Valentine's Day weather created the ideal Georgia afternoon sunshine to make the bride and bridesmaids, glow simply radiant. They looked liked true southern belles waiting for a garden party to begin or a formal evening social on the grounds of a country estate.

This very ground had supported the weight of many Confederate soldiers, slave owners, slaves and segregationists just generations before and bore much bloodshed, violence and tragedy throughout the years. Yet, it was as lovely a setting for Rebecca Murray Pope and Joe Lackey to capture the wedding party in their outdoor photos. The photo shoot not only documented the union between Horace Lee Miller and Christine Turner, it also represented the union between the "Old South" and a new chapter being written in the history of Macon County, Georgia.

The land and its stately pre-Civil War mansion that was built on the backs of Negro slaves had become a harbinger of the new racial and social tolerance in the Deep South. Surely the ghosts of generations of white southerners were likely hiding behind the grand old oak trees and peeking out at the scene that was taking place on the well-manicured lawns of Meade-Brown Mansion. Spirits of former slave owners were probably peering down from the attic dormer windows and wondering what was going on down below. Spirits of their former slaves were probably rejoicing and celebrating that the blood, sweat and tears of their labor and sacrifices had paved the way not only for Horace Lee and Christine in the "New South," but also for the newly elected President of the United States of America, Barack Hussein Obama.

"Hallelujah, free at last, free at last! Thank God, we is free at last!" echoed from the hallowed grounds of Meade-Brown Mansion and from the bauxite mines around Macon County, Georgia.

Inside, the Turner-Miller wedding reception guests enjoyed the ambience and comforts of a finely restored antebellum mansion. Meade-Brown Mansion when completed in 1839 was originally named the Thomas Archibald Meade House. The wedding reception guests congregated and attended a cocktail reception in the main hall that once served as the receiving area for the historic mansion's elaborate parties, sit-down dinners and social functions. During that period, the guests would arrive by horse-drawn carriage and enter through the grand entry portico of the Greek Revival home with stately columns and be greeted by a Negro butler. They would then be led to the drawing room, parlor, dining room, grand hall or ballroom. The home was inspired by the architectural drawings for Oak Alley Plantation in Vacherie, Louisiana done by architect Gilbert Joseph Pilie. As a southern statesman and textile merchant, Thomas Archibald Meade had traveled extensively. He had visited many stately homes and mansions throughout the South from New Orleans, Louisiana to Natchez, Mississippi, from Richmond, Virginia to Charleston, South Carolina, and he wanted to bring the same grand style to Macon County, Georgia. It took two years of construction to finish this lavish Montezuma home for him and his wife, Phyllis Clarke Meade. The grand home and land were passed down through generations of the Meade family.

His great-great grandson Tom Meade III renamed the home Meade-Brown Mansion when he met and fell in love with Robert Steven Brown. Thomas Archibald Meade would probably have burned the mansion down himself after the Civil War had he known what the future held in store for it. First his gay descendant was living openly with his lover, and then Negroes were being hosted as guests. The legacy and reputation of Thomas Archibald Meade as a Confederate gentleman and statesman had been ruined forever. The very notion that gays and blacks were now a part of the present and the future of Meade-Brown Mansion did not quite jive well with many people in Macon County.

Tom Meade III and Robert Steven Brown ignored the "rednecks" that taunted them or tried to put fear into them. These two men stood their ground instead of being effete men who succumbed to scare tactics. People around Montezuma respected them for that. The people who could not or would not accept their alternative lifestyle were the people who did not matter much to them anyway. They only cared about those who wrote the big checks for the use of Meade-Brown Mansion for weddings, receptions, parties and social functions. Money in their bank account more than made up for what people said behind their backs and for the evil that lived in wicked hearts of others.

The first social event ever to be held at the mansion took place on Easter Sunday 1839. Just after the completion of their palatial home, Thomas Archibald Meade and his wife, Phyllis Clarke Meade, hosted an Easter egg hunt on the grounds for their children and the children of their friends and neighbors. The lawn offered the perfect backdrop for southern belles dressed in the latest European fashions and Easter bonnets. Easter luncheon followed in the formal dining room. After the luncheon, Phyllis Clarke Meade provided an Easter meal for the servants and their children from the leftovers.

Approximately 100 years from that date on Easter Sunday, April 9, 1939, Philadelphia-born opera singer Marian Anderson, at the arrangement of Eleanor Roosevelt, wife of President Franklin Delano Roosevelt, gave a free concert performance on the steps of the Lincoln Memorial in Washington, D.C. to an integrated audience of 75,000. Ms. Anderson, a renowned contralto, had performed on many world stages yet she was denied the right to perform onstage at Constitution Hall in Washington, D.C. by the Daughters of the American Revolution because of the color of her skin. Mrs. Roosevelt resigned from the organization in support of Marian Anderson. Fannie Mae Turner used to tell her daughters about how she and her own mother had listened to the performance on the radio that Easter Sunday and what a proud day it was for Negro people everywhere. That performance symbolized the emerging social consciousness and racial equality in the United States, but not in Macon County, Georgia.

After the photo shoot was completed, Beverly Alexander ushered the wedding party into the grand hall through a side door and sat them at the head table to await the reception guests. Once they were situated, the doors to the grand hall opened and the wedding reception guests made their way to their respective tables in accordance with the seating chart so meticulously created by Marshall Tate. Only one person dared to violate his rules of proper etiquette, and that person was Carol Neptune, the town floozy with her young boyfriend in tow.

"Now wait a minute there, Missy! Just where in the hell do you think you is?" Marshall Tate bellowed out at her with his left hand placed firmly upon one hip and an index finger pointing straight at her. "Can't you read, Miss Thing? What table number is you supposed to sit your cradle-robbing ass down at?"

A quiet hush came over the entire room as Carol Neptune tried to cop a plea with him, "I just thought that we could sit over there by Edna Green and Dottie Fields?" She had now drawn them into the spotlight as well, a place that neither of them wanted to be. Both of them tried to hide from view behind the floral arrangement in the center of the table.

"Well you thought wrong! You better get your little, narrow ass back to where it's supposed to be, and take that boy with you. Don't mess with me. I ain't in no mood for your foolishness up in here!" he continued.

She beat a hasty retreat back to the table to which she had been assigned and sat down as she was told. Her face was as red as her dress. Carol Neptune's attempt to bypass the Marshall Tate system and his very public reprimand of her and her young boyfriend put everyone else on notice. Not another person got out of order nor did anyone else attempt to change seats. Marshall Tate had spoken, and he was not one to be fooled with nor did he suffer fools kindly.

After everyone was finally seated, Pastor Hicks blessed the gathering in preparation for the meal and festivities to follow.

"God bless the union between Horace Lee and Christine Miller and all of the people who have made this wedding day possible," he said. "Dear God, thank you for having provided such a beautiful day and for having graced these ceremonies with your almighty presence. Most of all, God bless the parents of Horace Lee and the memory of Henry and Fannie Mae Turner, for without them this day would not have happened."

The entire reception hall gave a resounding and rousing, "Amen."

It was now time for the Master of Ceremonies Marshall Tate to really shine along with his appointed assistants and best friends from Albany, Neesha and Wendy. As the wedding coordinator, he operated mostly from behind the scenes, but his talents were best suited to being out in front and the center of attention. The plan was for the three of them to direct the wedding reception like a stage play. The bride, groom, and their wedding party would be the main characters and the supporting cast, and the wedding guests would be an interactive audience. He had already warned Tom Meade III, Robert Steven Brown and Beverly Alexander that this would be unlike any other wedding reception that they had ever hosted at Meade-Brown Mansion. It would be something like "Tony and Tina's Wedding" meets "La Cage aux Folles" (The Cage with the Insane Ones) or Agatha Christie's Mystery Dinner Theater meets "The Bird Cage." The interactive wedding reception would take place while the wedding party and guests were dining on a meal inspired by the Sunday Supper cooking of Miss Fannie Mae Turner. The chef and his locally hired African-American sous chefs had cooked up a mess of Sunday supper vittles, including baked hen and dressing, collard greens, pole beans, yellow squash and cornbread. For dessert, they prepared rice pudding, and banana and bread pudding to serve in addition to the wedding cake made by Deloris Ellison. Fannie Mae would have been so honored and thrilled by all of their efforts if she were still alive.

Three of the wait staff dressed in red jackets served the head table. The five Turner sisters and the three brothers-in-law were quite surprised and comforted by the food placed before them. Cleophus Jones and Royce Jenkins envied them all for having known Fannie Mae Turner and her down-home cooking that was so lovingly prepared.

The Meade-Brown Mansion catering staff worked efficiently and expediently. A place card with the table number and seat number allowed the guests to indicate their baked hen preference of either light or dark meat. The cards were placed in front of each guest at the reception. They could also opt for an all-vegetable plate should they so desire. Many restaurants throughout the South offer what is a called "meat-plus-three," which is a choice of meat and an assortment of three types of vegetables. The wedding reception dinner emulating Fannie Mae Turner's Sunday Supper qualified as such. The waiters picked up the cards from each table, and the dinner plates started arriving soon afterwards. The table servers wasted no time in turning the requests into properly dispatched and correctly delivered plates of food that were sure to suit the satisfaction of each and every one of the guests. It was truly comfort food without a doubt, compliments of Horace Lee and Christine Miller in loving memory of Fannie Mae Turner.

Before the guests were seated, the wait staff had poured glasses of ice water, champagne and sweetened iced tea, which is another staple of the South.

Marshall Tate made an announcement to the guests, "You can drink all the sweet iced tea and water you want to, but do not, I repeat, do not touch the champagne until I say so."

As tempting as it was, no one dared to touch the champagne. Marshall Tate would be watching each and every one of them. Not one guest would dare risk receiving a lashing from the acid-tongued wedding coordinator like the one Carol Neptune got.

Horace Lee's best man, his brother Bobby Lee, gave the first toast.

He stood up and faced the newlyweds and said, "To Horace Lee and Christine, may your days of marriage be filled with much joy and happiness." He then looked at Christine and said, "Christine, I hope that you are able to stand him better than he is able to stand himself right now with his new hairdo!"

This brought laughter from throughout the room. Everyone in the place was so pleased that both Horace Lee and Christine had rid themselves of their dreaded Jheri-curls.

The head table and the guests raised their champagne glasses to toast the married couple. They were still not able to sip the champagne until instructed by Marshall Tate. His instructions were plain and simple, "When I say drink, you drink!" That was followed by his three finger snaps high up in the air in a big wide circle.

The response to that order resulted in "hisses" and "boos" throughout the room. Already primed with alcohol from the earlier cocktail reception, the guests wanted more.

Carol Neptune muttered, "That Bitch," under her breath.

"I heard that, Miss Thing. You better hope that you don't get arrested for kidnapping! Didn't I see your boy toy's picture on a milk carton? Officer John Henry Johnson, arrest that child molester," replied Marshall pointing at the offender.

She had once again raised the ire of Marshall Tate who could be extremely vicious when provoked, but this time it was all in good-natured fun. The whole room lit up in laughter again, all except for Carol Neptune and her young stud. He just buried his head in his hands from embarrassment and shame.

"Don't worry, Sugar, Miss Neesha will take you home with her tonight," said Marshall's friend from Albany to Carol's new beau. Carol just rolled her eyes at the very thought of it.

The next toast came from the maid of honor, Elenora, "To Christine, I think that I speak for all of your sisters, Belle, Nettie, Rosalie and me, our mother, Fannie Mae, would be so happy to know that Horace Lee finally bought the cow that he's been milking for so long."

Rosalie's loud roar of laughter got the whole gathering to clapping and stomping their feet. Even Nettie let out a "whoop!" This was the start of the interactive wedding reception that Marshall Tate had in mind. Everyone wanted in on the act.

Neesha was assigned to one side of the room with a microphone in hand, and Wendy took charge of the other side. Joe Lackey covered both sides with his video camera.

They recorded the heartfelt and warm well wishes and congratulations for the newlywed couple. Pastor Hicks and his wife, Ethel, wished that the couple's marriage would be as happy and long lasting as their own. Wayne Williams told them that he was looking forward to the day when he would find his own true love and happiness. There was a loud and audible gasp from most of the women, the faux women Neesha and Wendy, and from Marshall Tate himself. The most eligible bachelor in all of Macon County in South Georgia, perhaps in all of the state of Georgia, could finally be off the market forever. There would be a trail of tears and broken hearts strewn across every path wherever he had ever walked. Many women and even some men harbored a secret passion to be the chosen one of Wayne Williams. At this announcement, all they could do was to wish him well and hope that it did not come too soon. It would absolutely kill them to know that if he did, he would return to the city of his birth, Philadelphia, in search of a wife. For the faint of heart, he decided to leave that part out.

Horace Lee's cousin Alvin Watford offered Horace Lee and Christine a prayer, "Heavenly Father, I ask that you bless my cousin and his dear wife with the gifts of love and commitment, and most of all the gift of faith in you. Bless them, oh Lord, and keep them forever in your care. Help them to abide by the laws that govern their marriage: trust, honesty and fidelity." There was another unified and resounding, "Amen."

They also captured on videotape the comments of the funny and the absurd.

Helen Mills added, "Christine, girl, it is a good thing that you saw Horace Lee first; I like a tall drink of chocolate milk."

The Johnson twins, Purvis and Percival, both said to the new couple, "We thought from the time that we were little boys that we were going to marry Christine and Elenora Turner. Guess you all don't like small men." Purvis and Percival tended to speak the same thing at the same time just like most twins.

"What do you mean by 'small?'" shouted Marshall Tate.

"Small ain't the word. You two are still knee high to a grasshopper with stingers the size of a bumble bee," called out Dottie Fields in reference to their short stature and their male anatomy.

"You better hush your mouth, looking like Ronald McDonald's twin sister," was an insult hurled by Wendy at Dottie Fields. "Me and Neesha likes our men in any size that we can get 'em!"

Rosalie Tate could not help but to weigh in on this conversation. She never needed a video camera or microphone in her face to express her views.

But, Joe Lackey turned to her anyway as she shot back.

"My man, Esau, has got what it takes to satisfy this ole woman. There ain't no acupuncture going on down here!" Rosalie said as she swiveled her hips. "Bee stings my ass! Now, that's what you get when you're lucky, a man who can take care of his woman!"

Esau Tate never knew what was going to come out of the mouths of his wife and son. He just took it in stride.

The waitstaff of Meade-Brown Mansion could hardly keep a straight face as they tried to clear away the dinner plates. Realizing that things were beginning to deteriorate into the gutter, Marshall Tate wanted to avoid the possibility of his mother making any mention of the bride and groom with their matching gold teeth. That was a family matter to be dealt with only in private.

He gave the final toast. "Everyone raise your glasses. To my Aunt Christine, I thought that I would beat you to the altar, but I haven't found the right man yet and apparently you have. To my new Uncle Horace Lee, welcome to our family."

Everyone with raised champagne glasses cheered the newlyweds and drank with the permission of the wedding co-ordinator.

Marshall Tate gave DJ Cool Curtis Mo D the signal to start the music. "May I have your attention please? I present to you for the first dance, Mr. and Mrs. Horace Lee Miller."

As a specially mixed long-playing version of "You Make Me Feel Brand New" by Airrion Love and the Original Stylistics began to play, Horace Lee led his new bride to the dance floor. Midway through the song, all couples were invited to join in. Pastor Hicks and Ethel Hicks were the first to approach the dance floor. Elenora Turner and Royce Jenkins, Esau and Rosalie Tate, Joe and Nettie Bamo, Cleophus Jones and Carrie Lee Miller, Samuel and Hortense Miller followed them, and of course, Carol Neptune and her young man Jamaal. Eventually, the dance floor was nearly full. Not to be left out were the odd couples of Purvis and Neesha, and Percival and Wendy who walked onto the dance floor. Neesha and Wendy towered over their dance partners.

Finally, Cool Curtis Mo D did the unthinkable for Macon County, Georgia, "Please welcome to the dance floor Mr. and Mr. Tom and Robert Meade-Brown, our hosts for this evening." This was the first time that anyone could think of that a gay couple ever danced in public anywhere in the county. Tom Meade III and Robert Steven Brown would have to go all the way to Atlanta, Macon, Columbus or Savannah, Georgia just to dance together publicly in a gay club. They traveled to Atlanta each year for the annual Pride Festival in order to express their freedom and to unwind from the rigors of living in such a small community as Montezuma, Georgia. They felt oppressed and had experienced similar prejudices and bigotries as blacks had endured in Macon County.

The invitation for them to take to the dance floor of Meade Brown Mansion was totally unplanned and unscripted and caught everyone off guard. The two men walked onto the dance floor hand-in-hand to a thunderous applause.

This opened the door for the other big surprise of the evening, another couple reluctantly joined in with the couple's dance; it was Belle Turner and Adele Hammond who timidly walked onto the dance floor. While it is a typical phenomenon for women to dance together in many cultures, there was something quite special and more intimate in the way that Belle held Adele in her arms. Her sisters had always suspected that Belle had more than just a casual friendship with Adele. The two of them were always together whether it was visiting with Fannie Mae, grocery shopping, or just sitting together in church. While this was not unusual behavior for two women who had been close friends for so long, there was a real tenderness and a caring bond between them. Belle's younger sisters never questioned their older sister about her relationship with Adele. In the Turner household, Belle was like a third parent and received nothing but the honor and respect that she deserved from her younger siblings. Fannie Mae always treated Adele Hammond like another daughter. Her spirit was probably hovering above the dance floor, smiling down on all of her daughters, including Adele.

CHAPTER 21

FOREVER YOURS (PAID IN FULL)

After the couple's dance was over, the DJ announced all of the members of the wedding party starting with the maid of honor and bridesmaids, and then he announced the best man and the groomsmen. This was followed by Horace Lee's dance with his mother.

"This next song is dedicated to Mrs. Hortense Miller, mother of the groom, and to the late Fannie Mae Turner, mother of the bride, and to all of the mothers in the house," announced the DJ, Cool Curtis Mo D.

He then played "I'll Always Love My Mama" by the Intruders. Horace Lee escorted his mother to the center of the dance floor. They were joined by all five of the Turner sisters. The DJ invited all mothers to join in. The dance floor was packed full with all of the mothers and their dance partners, their sons and daughters.

Up next, he played a song by another Philadelphia singing group, Sister Sledge. Belle, Nettie, Rosalie, Christine and Elenora remained on the dance floor as the song "We Are Family" started to play. Marshall Tate joined his mother and aunts as they sang along and danced to the music. "We are family, I got all my sisters and me," they sang in perfect harmony with Elenora and Marshall singing the leads. This song had specific meaning for the Turner sisters; it was the song that they chose for a school talent contest where they had won first prize. Whenever and wherever the song is played, people jump to their feet immediately and just start dancing. The Turner-Miller wedding reception was no exception. The dance floor filled to capacity. "We Are Family" has become one of the greatest dance tunes and ultimate party songs of modern times. It is very popular at wedding receptions, anniversary parties, Bar Mitzvahs, Bat Mitzvahs, Sweet 16 parties and family reunions everywhere. You name the celebration, and this song is likely to be found on the playlist. The spirits of Thomas Archibald Meade and Fannie Mae Turner were probably doing a jig to "We Are Family" while hovering over the celebration down below. His Confederate past and heritage would be forever joined to this modern-day Negro woman in more ways than one.

Marshall Tate had orchestrated, along with the help of the DJ, a wedding-party-only dance. They chose two songs, one with a slow tempo and then another with a faster beat. Pastor Hicks and his wife, Ethel, Horace Lee and Christine, Esau and Rosalie, Joe Bamo and Nettie, Royce and Elenora, and Cleophus and Belle slow danced to Otis Redding's "Try a Little Tenderness." They next danced to Clarence Carter's "Slip Away."

After the wedding-party-only dance, the floor was opened to all of the guests. It became a tribute to the Motown legends of the '60s and '70s. DJ Cool Curtis Mo D played songs by Smokey Robinson and the Miracles ("Shop Around'); Martha Reeves and the Vandellas ("Heat Wave"); and Diana Ross and the Supremes ("Someday We'll be Together"). Marshall, Christine and Elenora repeated their rendition of the song the same way as they had done at the repast in the church hall after Fannie Mae's funeral. Marshall, of course, sang the Diana Ross lead. The Motown tribute also included tunes by The Four Tops, The Temptations, Stevie Wonder, The Marvelettes, Jr. Walker and the All Stars, Marvin Gaye and The Isley Brothers.

Lili Santa Maria Pfeiffer, Elenora's Uruguayan-born friend from New York, had her chance to dance when the DJ played Michael Jackson's "We Got to be Starting Something." The song with its strong Latin beat played directly to Lili's Spanish heritage. She grabbed the man seated nearest to her who just happened to be John Henry Johnson. Lili and John Henry did a hybrid mambo-calypso dance. John Henry was every bit as handsome and dashing as singer-actor Harry Belafonte. While watching them from the head table, Elenora thought to herself, "What a shame that I had to let him go." She also knew that many of the other guests were thinking the very same thing as she. She had noticed how people at the wedding and then the reception were closely watching whatever interactions were taking place between the two of them. For years after she left for New York, the town gossips continued to speculate and wonder about her and John Henry Johnson. Was he really Henry Turner's son? Was she pregnant by her own half-brother? Every small town has its gossips, but Oglethorpe, Georgia had more than its share.

Lili and John Henry Johnson started a conga line that snaked in and around the tables of guests picking up add-ons as they passed. The conga line resembled an anaconda slithering through the Amazon jungle with Lili in her red-satin dress and matching red-flowing Pashmina as its beautiful head; Wendy in her cherry-red Marilyn Monroe halter dress was in the center followed by Marshall Tate with his bright-red neck scarf. Neesha was at the tail of the snaking conga line dressed in her red Shantung Silk Mandarin Chinese ensemble. When the line reversed direction, now with Neesha at the head, it resembled a dragon in a Chinese New Year parade. Rebecca Murray Pope and Joe Lackey caught it all on video. This would be the most memorable wedding and reception that they had ever photographed and videotaped. It was also no doubt the most memorable for the Meade-Brown Mansion.

When it was time to cut the wedding cakes, the waitstaff of Meade-Brown Mansion, under the supervision of Deloris Ellison, wheeled the two decorated cake tables to the center of the dance floor. Horace Lee and Christine stood before the tables facing their wedding guests. Behind them was the remainder of the wedding party.

Horace Lee let out an, "Oh my God!"

It was not because of the breathtaking beauty of the three-tiered, white heart-shaped wedding cake with red piping and red interlocking hearts made of spun sugar; it was because of the groom's cake that Deloris Ellison had made especially for him. He was so impressed that the red-velvet cake was an exact replica of Michael Vick's #7 Atlanta Falcons' jersey. Red Velvet was his favorite cake and Michael Vick was still his favorite football player of all time. Horace Lee had remained a die-hard and devoted fan of the defamed and disgraced quarterback. And to that end, he remained committed to the idea that Michael Vick would one day return to professional football.

With her hand in his, they cut a small slice of the wedding cake that Christine fed to her husband. Then Horace Lee, with her hand on top of his, cut a very small piece of the groom's cake and fed it to his new bride. He was so psyched by the total appearance of his groom's cake that he was careful not to cut too deeply into the image of Michael Vick's jersey — the cake was going home with him. He would keep it in the freezer until his hero returned to the football field. Of course, he would leave room in the freezer for Christine's top layer of the wedding cake just as he had made room in his closets for her clothes when she moved in with him in Atlanta. After Joe Lackey videotaped the wedding-cake-cutting ceremony, Deloris Ellison supervised the removal of the cake tables back to the catering kitchen. There they removed the top tier of the wedding cake and stored it in the walk-in refrigerator along with the groom's cake, then they cut the bottom two layers of the wedding cake into slices and added them to the self-service dessert tables with the banana, bread and rice puddings. The guests helped themselves to the desserts, and the waitstaff poured coffee and hot tea and refilled the ice-water glasses.

DJ Cool Curtis Mo D continued to play soft jazz until it was time for the next act of the Turner-Miller wedding reception to begin. On cue from Marshall, he started playing Beyonce's "All the Single Ladies." All of the single ladies gathered on the dance floor for the tossing of the bouquet. This group was made up of every demographic of woman young and old, and even included those who were both real and imagined. Neesha, Wendy and Marshall were not going to be left out. Everyone anticipated that either Carol Neptune or Dottie Fields would be calling for a redo if one of the "fake women" from Albany, as they referred to them, or Marshall Tate caught the bouquet.

Dottie Fields, dressed in her Ronald McDonald attire, said to Carol Neptune when they were jockeying for position, "You'll have to get that boy's mama's permission in order to marry him!"

"Never you mind about my man, you better worry about getting one of your own," shot back Carol Neptune.

There had been a long running love-hate relationship and an unresolved feud between the two women, and the wounds had never healed. To this day, neither could remember why they even disliked one another in the first place. That is why Dottie found it so curiously odd when Carol wanted to be seated at the same table with her instead of the one to which she had been assigned, unless she just wanted to show off her younger man.

"Girls, girls you better behave now!" scolded Marshall Tate.

Christine got into a position on the dance floor that would favor either her sister Elenora or her sister Belle. It seemed that things were heating up between Elenora and Royce Jenkins, and

Belle and Adele were finally out of the closet. Belle was a little hesitant and apprehensive about such a public display of affection with Adele, but she was now free to be herself since both sets of their parents were now deceased. Her four sisters had to coax her to join in the bridal bouquet toss. With her back turned to the group on the dance floor, Christine gripped the silk version of her bridal bouquet tightly in her right hand. Before tossing the bouquet, she faked it twice in order to aim it in the direction that she wanted it to go. Each time that she faked it, she looked to see exactly where her sisters were standing. When Christine finally tossed the bouquet it headed straight for Dottie Fields who was standing in front of Elenora. Before she knew it, Carole Neptune knocked Dottie Fields to the floor, and Elenora Turner caught the bouquet flying in mid-air. The two archenemies lay sprawled on the floor in a tangled mass of red. Carol's short dress was up around her waist giving out more information than any decent woman ought to. Carol Neptune was giving out her name, address and ZIP code all at one time. She didn't care about being decent. She just wanted to stop Dottie from catching the bouquet. It was all caught on tape. Marshall Tate could not have choreographed this Kodak moment even if he had tried.

After Elenora caught the bridal bouquet, Royce Jenkins yelled out, "Yes!" He knew that he could out maneuver any of the other men to ensure that he caught the garter when Horace Lee tossed it. Royce had played basketball in high school and college. He sized up the competition as they came forward for the garter toss. Marshall Tate placed a chair in the center of the dance floor to which Horace Lee escorted his new wife. DJ Cool Curtis Mo D played "The Stripper" song as Horace Lee slowly moved his hand up Christine's right leg and beneath the skirt of her wedding suit. He teased everyone by pretending to pull the garter down her leg. Horace Lee kissed Christine's knee as he slid his hands back toward the intended target that was hidden just above the hemline of her skirt. When he finally extracted the elusive red garter with white hearts on it, there were cheers from the wedding reception guests.

Each of the single men positioned themselves to be the recipient of the prize being tossed by Horace Lee. He twirled the garter several times on the index finger of his right hand and then let it fly through the air. At that moment, all of the other men dropped down on one knee, leaving only Royce Jenkins standing. The garter landed right in his hands. This ploy on the part of his competitors was clearly the work of Marshall Tate. He had circulated word around the reception hall that if any single man other than Royce Jenkins caught the garter, that person would have to kiss him, Wendy and Neesha each three times on the lips — and to most of those other men, that seemed like a no-win situation and the kiss of death. It was not that they were at all homophobic; it was just that they did not want to endure the wrath of Marshall Tate. When Royce realized what had occurred, he was disappointed that he did not have the challenge of the competition from the others; but he was happy all the same and yelled out again, "Yes!"

Elenora Turner was escorted to the chair at the center of the dance floor where Royce Jenkins placed the garter on her leg, moved it upwards to her thigh, and kissed her on the lips to the cheers from all the wedding guests.

The two couples, Horace Lee and Christine and Royce and Elenora, took to the floor dancing to "You've Got a Friend" by Donny Hathaway and Roberta Flack. They were joined on the dance floor by many other couples, who were in love, or hoping to be in love. This was another opportunity for Tom Meade III and Robert Steven Brown to dance again in public, likewise for Belle Turner and Adele Hammond. The two alternative couples were accepted and embraced by just about everyone including Pastor Hicks. At the time, there were only four states where gay marriages were legal: Connecticut, Iowa, Massachusetts and Vermont. Barring a move to any of those states, gay couples in Macon County, Georgia would just have to wait patiently for things to change. Those in attendance at the Turner-Miller wedding reception who objected to the gay lifestyle remained silent and did not dare to express their negative opinions. Marshall Tate would not suffer their foolishness lightly.

The two cocktail bars that were closed during dinner and the wedding reception ceremonies, reopened and then open dancing began to signal that the evening would be winding down. For those who had attended alone or had not danced because of the lack of a dance partner, the DJ played back-to-back line dances, "The Electric Slide" and "The Cha-Cha Slide," which was right out of Lili Santa Maria Pfeiffer's Latin playbook. The tables emptied, and the dance floor became a sea of red. The Five Turner sisters, Marshall Tate, Wendy and Neesha were out in front leading the other dancers through the paces and steps to each of the line dances. Each time that they turned to move in another direction or to step, jump or hop forwards, backwards or side to side, the dresses on the women swung in rhythm with each movement. The line dances were always the highlight of a wedding reception and the chance for singles to show off their dancing skills. They were begging for more and DJ Cool Curtis Mo D gave them exactly what they asked for. The next two songs that he played were "Sweet Soul Music" by Arthur Conley and "Ain't That Peculiar Baby" by Marvin Gaye. The wedding party and the guests were sufficiently exhausted after such a workout.

Before the wedding reception ended, Pastor Hicks invited everyone to attend a prayer breakfast the next day at New Ebenezer First Missionary Baptist Church before their regular Sunday morning worship. The meal would be prepared by the church's Women's Auxiliary guaranteeing a truly southern breakfast, Fannie Mae Turner style. He also blessed the journeys of those who would be traveling both near and far. Many of the out-of-town guests would be staying locally before taking their drives back home or catching flights from Macon or Atlanta. Church members had opened the doors to their homes to accommodate the welcomed guests. Lili would be staying with her friend Elenora for a few days before returning back to New York. The Turners and the Millers provided extra space for out-of-town guests as well. Even Joe Bamo and Nettie opened their home to several family members who had not been able to attend Fannie Mae's funeral the month before. This was perfect since they lived right across the road from the cemetery, and their guests could visit her gravesite on Sunday morning before the prayer breakfast at New

Ebenezer First Missionary Baptist Church.

Beverly Alexander stepped to the microphone and thanked Horace Lee, Christine and Marshall Tate for selecting the Meade-Brown Mansion as the location for their wedding reception and for using the services of their house photographer, Rebecca Murray Pope. She then read a short proclamation before bidding the wedding party and their guests farewell. "We wish to thank the family of Fannie Mae Turner for allowing us the immense joy and pleasure of having hosted you and having served you on this most wonderfully blessed and happy occasion. We wish that she had lived long enough to see this day. In her honor, we also wish to thank you for allowing us to pay a debt that has been long overdue."

It was signed Love, Peace and Blessings, Tom Meade III, Robert Steven Brown and Rebecca Murray Pope. She then held up an envelope that contained the invoices for services rendered. The envelope was simply stamped PAID IN FULL. "We'll see you all at church in the morning."

Miss Fannie Mae's girls all looked at one another and smiled.

CHAPTER

22

MISS FANNIE MAE'S SUNDAY SUPPER COOKBOOK

POCKETBOOK ROLLS

from Virginia Banks

Ingredients

1 package active dry yeast
1/2 cup warm water
1/2 cup canned evaporated milk
1/3 cup sugar
1/3 cup shortening (Crisco)
1 tsp. salt
1 egg
3 1/2-4 cups all-purpose flour

Step 1: Preheat oven to 375 degrees.
Step 2: Scald milk, do not boil, and let cool until warm to the touch.
Step 3: In large mixing bowl, dissolve yeast in warm water (105-115 degrees), stir in two cups flour. Add sugar, shortening, salt, egg and milk. Beat until smooth. Mix in enough of remaining flour to make dough easy to handle.
Step 4: Cover with a dish towel (to keep the dough from drying out) in a warm place for one-and-one-half hours until dough rises to double in size.
Step 5: Spoon a large tablespoon amount of dough and roll in hands (lightly floured), flatten out and fold over in half. Place rolls on non-stick pan or cookie sheet, bake for 12-15 minutes until golden brown.

HOT-AND-SWEET SOUTHERN CORNBREAD

from Larry Batchelor

Ingredients

1 1/4 cup yellow cornmeal

1 cup self-rising flour

1/3 cup maple syrup or blackstrap molasses

1 cup milk (whole or low-fat)

2 tbsp. melted butter or margarine

1 egg

3 strips thick sliced or slab bacon (fried crisp and chopped into tiny bits)

2 jalapeño peppers (remove seeds, chop finely)

Step 1: Preheat oven to 400 degrees.

Step 2: Sift cornmeal and flour into large mixing bowl.

Step 3: Add chopped bacon bits and jalapeño peppers.

Step 4: Pour in milk and melted butter or margarine, stir to mix well.

Step 5: Add egg, stir to mix well.

Step 6: Pour in syrup or molasses, stir to mix well.

Step 7: Batter should be pourable, but not runny (add more milk if needed).

Step 8: Pour into non-stick baking pan or glass baking dish coated with vegetable spray.

Step 9: Bake approximately 20-25 minutes (stick a toothpick into center of cornbread, if it comes out clean it's done).

BAKED HEN AND DRESSING

from Larry Batchelor

Ingredients

1 4-5 lb. hen (remove giblets and neck, set aside)

2 cups water

2 eggs (beaten)

1 medium green bell pepper (chopped)

1 medium Vidalia onion (chopped)

1 cup cornbread (crumbled)

1 1/2 cup seasoned bread crumbs

3 tsp. salt

1 tsp. black pepper

1/3 cup butter

1 tbsp. cooking oil

2 tsp. garlic powder

2 tsp. onion powder

3 tsp. seasoning salt

3 tsp. Cajun seasoning

1 tsp. sage

Step 1 : Preheat oven to 400 degrees.
Step 2: Wash hen thoroughly; sprinkle one tsp. each of salt, black pepper and Cajun seasoning on top of hen and into cavity of hen.
Step 3: Wash giblets and neck, place in small saucepan, add two cups of water, one tsp. garlic powder, one tsp. onion powder, one tsp. seasoning salt, one tsp. Cajun seasoning, 1/2 tsp. sage. Bring to boil, simmer with lid on for about 15

minutes, remove pan from burner, and let cool.

Step 4: Melt butter in small skillet, add green pepper, onion, remaining seasonings. Sauté mixture until green peppers are softened and onions are translucent, remove from burner, and let cool.

Step 5: In a large mixing bowl, add crumbled cornbread, seasoned bread crumbs, stir to mix.

Step 6: Add sautéed mixture of butter, green pepper, onion and remaining seasonings, stir to mix well. Add beaten eggs, stir to mix in well; add giblet liquid from saucepan, stir to mix well and moisten dressing mixture. For a more moist stuffing mixture, add a little warm water.

Step 7: Before stuffing hen, heat one tbsp. cooking oil in a large cast iron skillet until hot, then sear the hen on all sides to seal in the juices.

Step 8: Place one cup of dressing mixture into cavity of hen and keep the remainder in a small greased baking dish and refrigerate.

Step 9: Place stuffed hen in a non-stick baking pan or vegetable-spray-treated, oven-ready glass dish, bake at 400 degrees for 30 minutes, reduce temperature to 350 degrees, and bake for another one hour and 25 minutes. Place refrigerated pan of dressing mix in oven with hen for the last 25 minutes.

SOUTHERN VEGETABLES (STRING BEANS, YELLOW SQUASH, POLE BEANS)

from Larry Batchelor

Ingredients

1 lb. fresh string beans (washed with ends cut), or

1 lb. yellow squash (washed and cut into 1/4 inch slices), or

1 lb. pole beans (washed and snapped)

Fannie Mae's Vegetable Boil (see below)

2 1/2 cups water

3 strips thick sliced/slab bacon (cut in cubes)

1 small yellow onion (diced)

1 tbsp. cooking oil

1/2 tsp. coarse kosher salt*

1/2 tsp. black pepper

1 tsp. seasoning salt*

1/2 tsp. cayenne pepper

**For low-sodium diet, substitute Mrs. Dash (original flavor)*

To make Fannie Mae's Vegetable Boil:

Step 1: In large pan, fry the bacon cubes in cooking oil until crispy, add diced onions and sauté until translucent, add kosher salt, black pepper, seasoning salt and cayenne pepper.

Step 2: Pour in water, add beans, yellow squash or pole beans, and cover and bring to a boil, lower to medium heat and simmer for 25-30 minutes or until done (tender pole beans take longer).

CAST-IRON SKILLET COOKED CREAM CORN

Ingredients

10 ears sweet corn (boil until tender, let cool), cut kernels from the cob, scrape the cob with a fork to get the milky liquid from the cob, and place in large bowl (for quick-and-easy version, use two large cans of sweet whole kernel corn drained)
3 strips thick sliced bacon/slab bacon (cut in cubes)
1 tsp. self-rising flour
1 tsp. salt
1 tsp. black pepper
1 tsp. sugar
1 tbsp. maple syrup
1/3 cup milk
1/3 cup water
bacon grease drippings (leave in pan)

Step 1: Add flour, salt, pepper and sugar to corn kernels in bowl, stir to mix well. In large cast-iron skillet, cook bacon cubes until crispy, lower heat, add corn mixture, stir and cook for one minute.
Step 2: Pour in milk and water and simmer for 10 minutes.

SHORTCUT CHICKEN AND DUMPLINGS

from Larry Batchelor

Ingredients

1 3-4 lb. whole chicken (remove giblets from cavity; wash thoroughly; sprinkle inside and out with a pinch of salt and pepper). Cut-up chicken parts can be used instead depending on preference (legs and thighs for dark meat lovers, wings or breasts for white meat lovers)
1 1/2 quarts water
3 cups Fannie Mae's Vegetable Boil (remove fried bacon cubes)
1 large can refrigerated biscuits

Step 1: In a large pot, prepare base for Fannie Mae's Vegetable Boil according to directions on page 210. Remove bacon cubes, add 2 1/2 cups of water and bring to a boil.
Step 2: Add whole chicken to the pot and pour in 1 1/2 quarts of water. Bring to a second boil; reduce heat to a medium simmer and let cook until chicken falls off the bone (add more water as needed).
Step 3: With a large skimmer, periodically skim fat from the top. Remove as many bones as possible and return to a rolling boil.
Step 4: Open can of biscuits, flatten each biscuit, cut into ½-inch strips and fold in half.
Step 5: Drop folded dumpling strips one by one into the boiling pot; cover; reduce to simmer and cook for approximately 8-10 minutes. Dumplings will float to the top when done. To check for doneness, cut dumpling with the

edge of a fork. The fork should cut right through.

Note: For an extra kick, slice one whole stalk of scallion (green onion) in ¼-inch slices and one large jalapeño pepper in 1/4-inch slices. Toss both into the pot at the same time as the folded dumpling strips.

Step 6: Serve up a heaping bowl of this Southern Comfort food without ever rolling in the dough! Miss Fannie Mae preferred the old-fashioned way of using a wooden rolling pin to make and flatten her dough and then cutting the dumplings into strips. Most houses today don't even have a rolling pin and have never heard of a wash scrub board for doing laundry. "Those were the good old days," Fannie Mae used to say.

MAPLE SUGAR SOUTHERN PECAN PIE

Ingredients

2/3 cup white granulated sugar
1/3 cup granulated maple sugar
1/2 cup light maple syrup
1 tsp. vanilla extract
1 8 oz. bag of pecan halves
1 cup unsalted butter (melted)
3 eggs (beaten)
1 9-inch unbaked pie shell (thaw frozen pie shell)

*__Note 1:__ For low-calorie, low-sugar or diabetic diet, use 1/2 of sugar amount with 1/2 sugar substitute (i.e., Splenda).
*__Note 2:__ Do not replace all of the sugar with a sugar substitute. This will affect the texture and browning in baking recipes. You may need to experiment by adjusting the sugar-to-sugar substitute ratio until satisfied. Miss Fannie Mae's desserts were as sweet as she was — there was no substitute!

Step 1: Preheat oven to 450 degrees.
Step 2: In large mixing bowl, combine sugars, syrup, vanilla extract and melted butter.
Step 3: Add pecans and beaten eggs to the syrup mixture. Stir well until mixed thoroughly.
Step 4: Pour pie filling mixture into pie shell and bake at 450 degrees for 10 minutes. Reduce temperature to 300 degrees and continue baking for an additional 35 minutes.

Note 3: For high-altitude baking (3,500 feet + above sea level), increase temperatures by 20 degrees and decrease baking time slightly. You may need to test this method until completely satisfied. Miss Fannie Mae Turner lived in Oglethorpe, Georgia, at an elevation of 341 feet above sea level. So don't blame her!

LEMON, SOUR CREAM AND VANILLA YOGURT POUND CAKE WITH LEMON GLAZE AND CHERRIES ON TOP

Ingredients

3 cups white granulated sugar

3 cups all-purpose flour

1/4 tsp. salt

1/4 tsp. baking soda

1 cup butter (softened)

2 tbsp. maraschino cherry juice (from small jar of cherries, reserve cherries)

1 4 oz. container sour cream

1 4 oz. container vanilla yogurt

2 tbsp. lemon juice

1/2 tsp. vanilla extract

3 large eggs

Step 1: Preheat oven to 325 degrees.

Step 2: Place all ingredients in a four-quart, stainless steel mixing bowl in the same order as above.

Step 3: Blend at a slow speed with a heavy-duty electric mixer for approximately one minute. While mixing, stop occasionally to scrape mixture from side of the bowl with a rubber spatula.

Step 4: Blend on medium speed for approximately two more minutes.

Step 5: Spoon blended cake batter into a lightly greased and floured 10-inch Bundt pan.

Step 6: Bake at 325 degrees for one and one-half hours or until done (when a toothpick is stuck in and comes out clean).

Step 7: Leave cake in Bundt pan and cool for 10 minutes.

Step 8: Remove cake from pan and place on cake plate.

Step 9: Drizzle with lemon glaze (recipe below) and top with leftover maraschino cherries.

Step 10: Lemon Glaze: Mix together one cup powdered sugar, two tbsp. lemon juice, and 1/2 tsp. vanilla extract.

Note: Make adjustments for high-altitude (3,500 ft. + above sea level) baking. The normal rule is simple: "increase temperature by 20 degrees, reduce baking time slightly." That's all that Miss Fannie Mae can tell you. There are no mountains in Oglethorpe, Georgia!

OLD FASHIONED BANANA RAISIN RICE PUDDING

from Larry Batchelor

Ingredients

2 cups long grain rice (cooked)
2 large bananas (diced into small pieces)
3/4 cup sweet raisins
1 small package instant vanilla or banana pudding mix
1 cup granulated sugar
1/2 tbsp. nutmeg
1/2 tbsp. ground cinnamon
1/2 tbsp. vanilla extract
3 eggs (well beaten)
2 cups canned evaporated milk

Step 1: In large bowl combine rice, banana pieces, raisins, pudding mix, sugar, nutmeg and cinnamon. Stir to mix well.
Step 2: Add vanilla extract, beaten eggs and evaporated milk. Stir to blend well.
Step 3: Add more evaporated milk for creamier consistency.
Step 4: Pour mixture into a large, non-stick baking dish.
Step 5: Bake in a 375-degree oven for 30-35 minutes.
Step 6: Serve warm or chilled.

Miss Fannie's Mae's girls prefer this dessert served hot, but the taste of the leftovers (if there are any) after being chilled is amazing.

PEACH BREAD PUDDING

(Why not? After all Miss Fannie Mae Turner was born in the "Peach State.")

Ingredients

8 cups dry bread (use leftover biscuits and bread pieces, break into medium-sized pieces)
2 cups diced canned peaches (reserve ½ cup peach liquid)
1/2 cup white or sweet raisins
2 cups of canned evaporated milk
2 cups half-and-half (you can substitute whole milk or low-fat milk)
2/3 cup granulated sugar
1 tbsp. cornstarch
1/4 tsp. salt
1/2 tbsp. ground cinnamon
1/2 tbsp. nutmeg
2 large eggs (beaten well)
3/4 cup chopped pecans or walnuts (optional)

Step 1: Preheat oven to 375 degrees.
Step 2: Mix bread, peaches, and raisins in large bowl until blended well.
Step 3: Pour mixture into large greased or non-stick baking pan.
Step 4: In a saucepan on low heat, blend canned milk and half-and-half and heat until warm.
Step 5: In a separate bowl, combine eggs, reserved peach liquid,

sugar, cinnamon, nutmeg and cornstarch.

Step 6: Pour in the warm milk and half-and-half, blend well.

Step 7: Pour this mixture over bread mixture in baking pan. Sprinkle the top with pecans or walnuts and cover with aluminum foil.

Step 8: Bake at 375 degrees for 35 minutes. Serve warm.

Like Miss Fannie Mae's Banana Raisin Rice Pudding, this dish is excellent served warm or cold. Tastes even better when ingredients are mixed with loving hands!

Optional: For those who like a little kick, spoon Bourbon Sauce (recipe below) over warm bread pudding.

Bourbon Sauce: In a small saucepan combine one cup whipping/heavy cream, one tsp. vanilla flavor, 1/3 cup maple syrup, 1/3 cup sugar and 1/3 cup bourbon. Warm slowly, stirring constantly.

HOMEMADE PEACH ICE CREAM

Ingredients

1 lb. fresh peaches (peeled and cut into small chunks)
1 tsp. natural peach flavor or peach extract
1/2 cup organic peach nectar
1 tsp. vanilla flavor
6 eggs (well beaten)
2 pints whipping cream
1 can Pet Evaporated Milk
1 cup extra fine granulated sugar
Whole milk (a quantity that is enough to fill remainder of 1 gallon ice cream freezer)

Step 1: Place fresh peaches in a glass dish with lid.
Step 2: Add peach flavor or extract and peach nectar, cover and marinate overnight in refrigerator.
Step 3: Put beaten eggs in blender, add sugar and add about two cups whole milk, and blend well.
Step 4: Pour into large bowl then add whipping cream, Pet Evaporated Milk and vanilla flavor. Mix thoroughly.
Step 5: Pour into ice cream freezer, add peach mixture then fill ice cream freezer to capacity with whole milk.
Step 6: Follow ice cream freezer instructions.

Miss Fannie Mae Turner was truly a Georgia Peach, pure and sweet.

QUICK-AND-EASY PEACH COBBLER

Recipe can be modified for Apple Cobbler using apples and apple juice, or Blueberry Cobbler using blueberries and natural blueberry juice.

Ingredients

1/2 cup unsalted butter (softened)
1 cup all-purpose flour
2 cups granulated sugar
1 tbsp. baking powder
pinch of salt
1 cup milk
4 cups fresh peaches (peeled and sliced)*
1 tbsp. lemon juice
1/2 tsp. peach extract or flavor
1/4 cup of organic peach nectar
1 tsp. ground nutmeg and 1 tsp. ground cinnamon (mixed)

Step 1: Preheat oven to 375 degrees.
Step 2: Combine flour, one cup of sugar, baking powder, and salt in large bowl; add milk, stirring just until the dry ingredients are moistened.
Step 3: Spread softened butter in baking dish.
Step 4: Pour batter mixture over butter into baking dish; do not stir.
Step 5: Heat remaining one cup of sugar, peach slices, peach nectar, peach extract/flavor and lemon juice in saucepan until

bubbly, stirring constantly.

Step 6: Pour hot peach mixture over batter mixture in baking dish; do not stir. Sprinkle the top with the nutmeg and cinnamon mixture.

Step 7: Bake at 375 degrees for 40-45 minutes until golden brown.

***Note:** Fannie Mae always had home-canned peaches stored in Mason jars on hand for any dessert or dish that required them. If you are too busy to peel and slice fresh peaches or to can and store them in Mason jars, use four cans of store-bought peaches (drained, use reserved liquid instead of peach nectar).

CHAPTER 23

THE NEW EBENEZER FIRST MISSIONARY BAPTIST CHURCH WOMEN'S AUXILIARY COOKBOOK

BAKED HAM

from Helen Prysock

Ingredients

8-10 lb. ham

1 cup brown sugar

1/2 cup honey

1 tbsp. spicy brown mustard

1 tbsp. cinnamon

2 cups of orange juice*

1 small can mandarin oranges*

Step 1: Preheat oven to 325 degrees.
Step 2: Remove some skin from ham, and leave some fat on.
Step 3: Place ham in large baking pan, and poke deep holes in top of ham with large fork.
Step 4: Combine brown sugar, honey, spicy brown mustard, cinnamon, and 1/2 cup of orange juice in sauce pan. Heat over medium temperature, stir until mixture is combined well, about two minutes. Pour and spread mixture over ham.
Step 5: Pour one-and-one-half cups of orange juice in bottom of baking pan.
Step 6: Place mandarin orange slices over top of ham.
Step 7: Bake uncovered in a 325-degree oven for one-and-a-half hours, basting with pan juices every 30 minutes.
***Note:** Substitute pineapple juice and canned pineapple chunks or apple juice and apple sauce.

FRIED CHICKEN

from Deloris Ellison

Ingredients

3-4 lbs. assorted frying chicken pieces (legs, thighs, breasts, wings)
2 cups self-rising flour
1 tbsp. salt
1 tbsp. black pepper
1 tbsp. paprika
vegetable oil or canola oil enough to fill skillet or frying pan half-full
1 tbsp. butter
1 medium-large brown paper bag

Step 1: Wash and rinse chicken well, remove excess water with paper towels and leave moist.
Step 2: Combine flour, salt, black pepper and paprika in paper bag; shake closed bag well to mix.
Step 3: Preheat vegetable oil or canola oil over high heat in covered cast-iron skillet or heavy frying pan.
Step 4: Add butter to hot oil.
Step 5: Shake pieces of chicken in brown paper bag until well coated.
Step 6: Place chicken pieces into hot-buttered oil and cover.
Step 7: Fry on medium-to-high heat until golden brown and crispy, about 10-14 minutes.
Step 8: Remove cooked chicken pieces to plate with paper towels to drain excess oil.
Step 9: Place on serving platter.

SPICY OVEN-FRIED BAKED CHICKEN

from Ethel Young

Ingredients

4-5 lbs. assorted chicken pieces (legs, thighs, breasts, wings)
1 tsp. onion powder
1 tsp. garlic powder
1/2 tsp. salt*
1 tsp. black pepper
1/2 tsp. seasoning salt*
1 tsp. Cajun seasoning*
1/4 cup soy sauce (low-sodium)
1/4 cup Italian dressing (low-sodium)
1 tbsp. cooking oil

Step 1: Preheat oven to 400 degrees.
Step 2: Wash chicken thoroughly and drain on paper towels. In a small bowl, combine the onion powder, garlic powder, salt, pepper, seasoning salt and Cajun seasoning.
Step 3: Place chicken pieces in large bowl, coat with soy sauce and Italian dressing; sprinkle each piece with seasoning mixture.
Step 4: Before placing seasoned chicken in the oven, heat one tbsp. of cooking oil in large cast-iron skillet until hot; sear chicken pieces on all sides to seal in the juices.
Step 5: Place chicken pieces in a large non-stick baking pan or pan coated with vegetable spray.
Step 6: Bake chicken uncovered at 400 degrees for 30 minutes.

Lower temperature to 350 degrees and continue baking for approximately 45 minutes to one hour. Remove from oven when done (juices run clear when pricked with a fork).

Step 7: Let stand for five minutes. Drain chicken on paper towels and transfer to serving platter.

*__Note:__ For low-sodium diet, substitute Mrs. Dash Original Seasoning.

BLACK-EYED PEAS, CORNBREAD CASSEROLE

from Loretta Wilson

Ingredients

1 lb. bag of black-eyed peas cooked according to directions

1 lb. ground beef, browned and drained

1 large onion, chopped

1 large green pepper, chopped

2 cloves of minced garlic

1 can of crushed or diced tomatoes

1 cup cooked rice

2 packages of corn bread mix (prepare according to directions and set aside)

Salt and pepper to taste

Note: For a spicier dish, you may add two seeded jalapeño peppers finely chopped into ground beef.

Step 1: Preheat oven to 350 degrees.

Step 2: In a skillet, brown ground beef with onions, garlic and green pepper. Stir occasionally. Cook five minutes.

Step 3: Drain the ground beef and set aside.

Step 4: In a 9x13-inch casserole dish, layer ½ of the cornbread mixture to cover the bottom of the pan. Add ground beef mixture, crushed tomatoes and rice.

Step 5: Add black eyed peas and spread evenly.

Step 6: Spread the remaining cornbread mixture on top.

Step 7: Bake at 350 degrees for 20 minutes or until cornbread is done.

***Note:** A staple in the Southern diet for over 300 years, black-eyed peas have long been associated with good luck.

OKRA, TOMATO, CORN AND BLACK-EYED PEA SUCCOTASH

from Larry Batchelor

Ingredients

1/2 lb. fresh okra (washed and cut horizontally in 1/4" slices, set aside)*

1 lb. small fresh whole tomatoes (washed and cut in quarters, set aside)*

4 ears yellow or white corn (boiled and cut kernels from the cob, set aside)*

1 lb. package black eyed peas (prepare according to directions, set aside)*

Note: "Some Southerners like it hot"

1 large jalapeño pepper (sliced, optional)

1 tsp. hot sauce/Tabasco sauce

3 cups Fannie Mae's Vegetable Boil with crispy slab bacon (prepare in large pot according to directions on page 210 of Fannie Mae's Sunday Supper Cookbook)

Step 1: Prepare Fannie Mae's Vegetable Boil in large pot, add fresh okra and tomato quarters; bring to a boil, reduce heat and simmer for 20 minutes. Add cooked corn, black-eyed peas, jalapeño pepper and hot sauce. Stir to blend well and simmer for 20 minutes more.

Step 2: For the quick-and-easy method, start with 1 1/2 cups of Fannie Mae's Vegetable Boil, get out your handy electric can opener and substitute one 8 oz. can cut okra, one 16 oz. can diced tomatoes, one 16 oz. can whole kernel corn (drained), and two 8 oz. cans of black eyed peas.

Step 3: Add all ingredients to vegetable boil.

Step 4: Bring to a boil then reduce to a simmer. Cook for 35-45 minutes.

***Note:** If you prefer to use frozen vegetables, use the same portions of frozen vegetables except for the tomatoes. Follow the same instructions.

SOUTHERN STYLE POTATO SALAD

from Edna Thompson

Ingredients

5 lbs. white potatoes (peeled and cut into approx.
1" x 1" cubes)
6 boiled eggs (cooled, diced/chopped)
1 6 oz. jar sweet pickle relish or sweet pickle cubes
1 tbsp. celery seeds
1/2 tsp. salt
1/3 cup granulated sugar
1/3 cup white vinegar
*1 1/2-2 cups mayonnaise
3 tbsp. yellow mustard
paprika
1 medium white/yellow onion (diced/chopped, optional)

Step 1: Boil peeled and cubed white potatoes uncovered in large pot until tender (pierce lightly with fork to determine if done).
Step 2: Drain potatoes well in large colander; place in refrigerator to cool down and stiffen.
Step 3: In a large mixing bowl, add potatoes, diced/chopped boiled eggs, relish/pickle cubes, celery seeds, sugar, salt and vinegar. Add chopped onion if desired.
Step 4: Mix ingredients together lightly with a rubber spatula or wooden spoon.

Step 5: Add mayonnaise and mustard; mix with spatula/spoon until all ingredients are thoroughly blended. Taste for desired sweetness or tartness. Add additional sugar or vinegar to adjust to desired taste.

Step 6: Place in serving dish, sprinkle top with paprika, and refrigerate until ready to serve.

*__Note:__ Use smaller amount of mayonnaise for dryer potato salad, more for creamier consistency.

SWEET POTATO LEMON PIE

from Sandra Mabry

Ingredients

4 medium sweet potatoes (cooked, peeled, when using fresh potatoes remove strings) or use 2 16 oz. cans sweet potatoes (drained)

2 1/2 cups sugar

3/4 cup butter

3 eggs

1 package instant lemon pudding mix (dry)

1 12 oz. can evaporated milk*

1 tbsp. vanilla extract or imitation vanilla flavoring

1 tsp. lemon extract or imitation lemon flavoring

1 tsp. cinnamon

1 tsp. allspice or nutmeg

2 frozen 9-inch pie shells

Step 1: Preheat oven to 350 degrees. Place cookie sheet in oven to heat.

Step 2: In a large mixing bowl, mash sweet potatoes, add butter and mix together.

Step 3: Add sugar, lemon pudding mix, vanilla flavor, lemon flavor, cinnamon and allspice.

Step 4: In another bowl, beat eggs and add milk.

Step 5: Pour eggs and milk over sweet potato mixture stir well to combine completely.

Step 6: Pour into pie shells, place on cookie sheet and bake for approx. 45-50 minutes or until done.**

***Note:** Can substitute whole milk.

****Note:** Increase baking time in high-altitude areas.

BERRY, BANANA, PEACH TRIFLE

from Larry Batchelor

Ingredients

3 Angel Food cake rings

1 lb. container vanilla-flavored yogurt

1/2 pint fresh strawberries

1/2 pint fresh blueberries

1/2 pint fresh blackberries

3 bananas

1 8 oz. can sliced peaches drained (reserve liquid)

1 bag chopped walnuts

2 oz. Peach Schnapps liqueur (optional)

Step 1: Wash, rinse and drain berries; remove stems from strawberries and slice.
Step 2: Combine all berries together in a bowl.
Step 3: Add Peach Schnapps to the reserved liquid from peaches.
Step 4: In a large glass trifle bowl with pedestal base, make three layers of the ingredients as follows.
Step 5: Place the Angel Food cake ring in the bottom of bowl. Drizzle peach liquid over cake top.
Step 6: Using a spatula, spread the cake top with vanilla-flavored yogurt allowing it to drip into cake ring hole.
Step7: Sprinkle chopped walnuts over yogurt.
Step 8: Slice one banana on top of yogurt and chopped walnuts.
Step 9: Spoon the berry mixture over banana, yogurt and

chopped walnuts and into cake-ring hole.

Step 10: Repeat the above steps over each layer of the Angel Food cake ring.

Step 11: Cover bowl with plastic wrap.

Step 12: Refrigerate until ready to serve.

PINEAPPLE COCONUT CAKE

from Sandra Mabry

Ingredients

1/2 lb. butter (softened)

3-3/4 cups confectioner's sugar

1 cup buttermilk

1 tsp. clear vanilla flavoring

3 cups self-rising flour

1/2 cup butter (softened, not melted)

2 cups sugar

1 sm. can crushed pineapple (drain and save juice)

4 eggs

1 tsp. vanilla extract or imitation vanilla flavoring

2 cups shredded coconut

Cake:

Step 1: Preheat oven to 350 degrees.

Step 2: In a large mixing bowl, with an electric or hand mixer, cream butter and sugar together, blending until smooth.

Step 3: Separate egg yolks and whites. Place egg whites in refrigerator.

Step 4: Add one egg yolk at a time into sugar and butter mixture and blend. Add vanilla flavoring.

Step 5: Alternately add flour and buttermilk into sugar, and butter mixture and continue to blend.

Step 6: Beat/whisk egg whites and then fold/blend into batter.

Step 7: Grease and flour a cake pan, then pour in batter; bake at 350 degrees for 40-45 minutes or until done (test for doneness with toothpick in middle; if it comes out clean, cake is done).
Step 8: Remove cake from cake pan, place on cake serving plate, and set aside.

Frosting and Center:
Step 1: In mixing bowl, cream softened butter, add confectioner's sugar, vanilla flavoring, and juice from crushed pineapples. Blend all ingredients until smooth and fluffy.
Step 2: Add more sugar to adjust consistency.
Step 3: Smooth icing over the entire cake. Place crushed pineapples in center of iced caked. Sprinkle coconut on and around the entire cake.

ACKNOWLEDGEMENTS

First and foremost I would like to give thanks to my grandmother, Rosalie Kleckly Batchelor, to whom this book is dedicated. She was always a great inspiration to me in life, and still is long after her death. By the way, Rosalie had eight children of her own, five daughters and three sons, who loved her as dearly as I did. I thank my mother, Edna Thompson, my aunts Ethel Young and Helen Prysock, and my devoted cousin Helen Mills for always believing in me. In their eyes I can do no wrong, to which I wholeheartedly disagree. Thanks also to my other parents: my two Dads, John Eddings (Carole) and George Thompson (Loretta); they too have been a tremendous source of support and inspiration throughout my life.

I must give special thanks to my dear close friends Dr. Ernest C. Wynne III, M.D. and Nathaniel "Nate" Hill. It was in their guest bedroom on Capitol Hill (Washington, DC) on New Year's Day, January 1, 2009, that the first chapter of "Miss Fannie Mae's Girls" was written. Many thanks to other dear friends and family members who have allowed me to talk incessantly about this book and those of you who have offered your "unbiased" opinions, to which I also disagree that your opinions were unbiased: Hebert Alexandre Cabral Da Costa, Wayne Williams, Robert Jones, Carol Neptune, Anita Robinson, Carolyn Adams, Melvin "Toney" Cason, Robin Hammond, Delores Williams, Daniel D. Ware (deceased), Doris Sherard, Christine Lewis, Robert Dixon, Milton Simpson, Edwin Lohr, Stacey Pearson, Ron Gay, Dara Francis, Delores Batchelor, my brother Steven I. James, and most of all to my cousin Allen Batchelor who is also like a brother and who tolerated me when he could not escape the loft that we once shared. Having to listen to me talk on and on about "Miss Fannie Mae's Girls" is probably the reason that we are no longer roommates today. Allen was responsible for introducing me to his friend, author Norma Jennings, who in turn was instrumental in introducing me to Michelle Gamble-Risley of 3L Publishing.

It was after meeting Michelle Gamble-Risley at the launch of Norma's book "Daughter of the Caribbean" in South Beach, Miami that I found my voice. Michelle nurtured and coached me throughout this arduous process. She encouraged me to move forward and to persevere. For this I give great thanks and gratitude to her and also to Malia Grigsby and Erin Pace (book designer) for their tireless work in bringing "Miss Fannie Mae's Girls" to life. I am looking forward to a long and rewarding professional relationship with 3L Publishing. They have delivered as promised on "Miss Fannie Mae's Girls" and I look forward to sending more manuscripts their way. Thank you, Michelle!

I wish to thank those of you who approved of and honored me by granting your permission to pay tribute to you by using your names as attendees at the funeral of Fannie Mae Turner and the wedding guests of Horace Lee Miller and Christine Turner.

I wish to thank those who contributed their recipes for the "Miss Fannie Mae's Sunday Supper Cookbook" and "The New Ebenezer First Missionary Baptist Church Women's Auxiliary Cookbook": Virginia Banks, Deloris Ellison, Edna Thompson, Sandra Mabry, Ethel Young, Helen Prysock, Loretta Wilson.

Finally, I want to thank you, dear reader, for spending some time with Miss Fannie Mae and her girls: Belle, Nettie, Rosalie, Elenora, and Christine, and of course, let's not forget Marshall Tate of Albany, Georgia.

Kind regards,

Larry Batchelor

ABOUT THE AUTHOR
LARRY BATCHELOR

MARTIN REGUSTERS-LEAPING LION PHOTOGRAPHY

The author was born and raised in Philadelphia, Pennsylvania. Larry spent his formative years living in the city and spending his summers at his Grandmother Rosalie's farm in Southern New Jersey. Down the road was her father Henry Kleckly's farm. Larry's great-grandfather Henry lived to be 106 years old; he was the oldest living resident of Atlantic County, New Jersey at the time of his death. Old man Henry, who nicknamed Larry "Grasshopper" and "Stinging Worm," once called his great-grandson an "old man in a young man's body." Henry Kleckly was such a colorful and interesting man of African-American and Native-American descent that he easily became one of Larry's earliest influences in character studies. His grandmother Rosalie, who passed away in 1993, still remains a driving force in his life; he named two of the boats that he has owned Rosalie I and Rosalie II.

It was those summer trips to the country to visit his grandmother and great-grandfather as well as vacation trips to the New Jersey shore that developed Larry's thirst for adventure and travel. Many young people growing up in urban areas of Philadelphia at the time rarely strayed outside the boundaries of their own ethnic neighborhoods, but Larry was allowed to wander and explore the greater multi-ethnic world beyond. His independence and exploration opened up a world of imagination, which led to his desire to write books. While attending Central High School for Boys, a college preparatory school for gifted students, Larry's favorite classes were English Literature, Composition, World History and Art History; and his favorite place to be on campus was the Barnwell Library, perusing through books, magazines and newspapers from around the globe. His world continued to expand and broaden beyond his inner-city roots.

After graduation he pursued studies in journalism and spent a summer interning at the Boston Record American newspaper. After a summer of exploring Boston, the New England countryside and Cape Cod, his sights quickly changed to business administration and marketing, which led him to leave behind his dreams of becoming a writer or journalist. But, his yearnings for travel and writing never waned. While traveling throughout Germany in 1987, he purchased his first journal in Berlin where he started writing his unpublished memoirs, "The Backstairs of My Life." Larry has written parts of his life's experiences and has jotted down his many ideas for future books set in faraway places, from the South of France to Russia, from Spain to St. Lucia, from Charleston in South Carolina to Brazil in South America.

Larry has enjoyed a very successful career in marketing, advertising, and sales which has only allowed him to write in his spare time. However, while in between jobs and full-time employment, he began writing his first novel, "Miss Fannie Mae's Girls."

Mr. Batchelor's second novel is currently a work in progress.